Object Storage for Genomics

Deploying and administering OpenStack
Swift with SwiftStack for bioinformatics

by Joe Arnold
forward by Chris Dagdigian, The BioTeam Inc.

Table of Contents

Chapter Eight
Hardware Deployment with SwiftStack

Afterword

Object Storage for Genomics

Deploying and administering OpenStack Swift with
SwiftStack for bioinformatics

Foreword

By Chris Dagdigian, The BioTeam Inc.

Over the last few decades, life sciences has been transformed into a field where discovery and application are driven more and more by technologies that generate larger and larger datasets at increasing rates. This trend is strikingly evident in the area of genomics where ever-improving DNA sequencing instruments have seen a rapid growth in throughput, resulting in decreasing costs for sequencing genomes. As the understanding of genomics has advanced due to the newfound accessibility of genomic sequence data, this has had far reaching implications, one of the most notable being in the area of personalized medicine. Now that the ability to sequence every patient's genome to provide more targeted care is slowly but surely becoming a reality, the challenges and bottlenecks associated with inadequate infrastructure to support such a data intensive endeavor are becoming painstakingly clear.

To put things into context, let's say that a single whole human genome sequence dataset is 200GB of data. Consider the implications of this when trying to sequence hundreds of thousands of patients. If careful thought is not put into data storage, it can lead to costly infrastructure mistakes. It is clear that, just as there were technological advances that accelerated the adoption of genome sequencing into the scientific and clinical communities, corresponding advances need to be made with respect to data storage in order to enable the continued growth of genomics.

Commoditization Drives Data Volume

The rapid innovation in genome sequencing technology is driving down the cost of acquiring genomic data at a rate that exceeds Moore's Law.

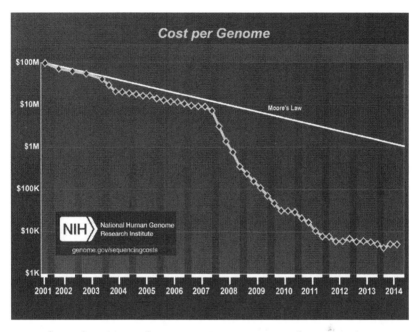

Data from the National Human Genome Research Institute's Genome Sequencing Program http://www.genome.gov/sequencingcosts/ Figure 0-1

The low cost has made sequencers affordable for small labs and individual researchers who are deploying them in locations that may not be well served by organizational network, storage, and compute resources. At the same time, organizations do not traditionally "bank" cost savings realized by cheaper sequencing platforms – many simply purchase more platforms and generate more raw data! The end result has been an explosive increase in raw data that threatens to swamp even the most prepared. Unfortunately, the cost of raw storage capacity is not decreasing as rapidly as sequencing costs. The blunt reality today is that scientists can generate massive volumes of data and the cost of producing or acquiring this data is less than the real world cost of storing, managing, and securing it.

The life sciences have reached an important tipping point where it is cheaper to generate data than it is to store and manage it through a standard lifecycle. New methods, techniques, and technologies are required. Open source storage projects like OpenStack Swift when combined with low-cost storage hardware provide relief for the storage challenges faced by life sciences.

Beyond simple cost relief, object storage also has entirely new capabilities not easily available with the traditional "files and folders" way of storing and accessing digital information. A key inherent feature of this new class of storage is the ability to associate arbitrary tags, information, and metadata with the files being stored. This new way to store, reference, and search upon custom user-supplied metadata associated with the data being stored is a **transformative** "force-multiplier" for anyone who needs to produce, manage, organize, or consume vast amounts of information.

Let's examine what "metadata" we can associate with files in the standard "files and folders" view of a POSIX compliant Linux filesystem:

- Owner
- Group
- Read/Write/Execute permissions based on Owner and Group settings
- File size
- Creation/Modification/Access timestamps

Those are all useful attributes, to be sure, but what about all of the other essential information that needs to be tracked per-file, per-experiment, per-trial, or for every genome sequencing instrument run? Information like:

- What instrument produced this data?
- What grant or funding source paid for the production of this data?
- What hardware/flowcell/technology revision was in place on the instrument ?
- Who is the primary PI or owner of this data?
- Who are the secondary and tertiary data owners should the

primary owner separate from the organization?

- What protocol was used to prepare the sample?
- Where did the sample come from?
- What program, experiment, patient, or clinical trial is this sample associated with?
- Where is the consent information for this trial/experiment stored?
- Can this data be used to identify a patient or individual?
- How rare is this sample? Is re-sequencing an option?
- What is the data retention classification for this file?
- What is the security classification for this file?
- Can this file be moved offsite?
- Can this file be moved between countries or other jurisdictional boundaries?
- And anything else that would be useful to your organization.

Right now the life science researchers have to track all of the essential "metadata" using external systems that are often physically and logically separated from the actual data. LIMS systems, sample tracking systems, relational databases, and many other complex "metadata aware" systems have been developed from scratch to address these problems. Few do it well and almost all successful implementations require non-trivial levels of dedicated hardware as well as full time development, engineering, and operational staff.

The ability to natively associate custom organizational-specific "metadata" with the files flowing into an object store is obviously interesting. What turns object storage from **interesting** into **transformative** is the ability to use the user-supplied custom metadata as the basis for search queries. The ability to search, view, organize, and sort based on user-supplied metadata is the primary reason why BioTeam believes that the future of all scientific data storage will be object-based.

As you read this book, you will come to learn and understand the storage workloads faced by next-generation sequencing and how OpenStack Swift addresses those issues. The team at SwiftStack has brought their experience to OpenStack Swift to make it easy for institutions to adopt and deploy this new storage option.

We at BioTeam make a habit of tracking disruptive technologies in order to help our clients and facilitate our own work. We are truly excited about what this new technology will allow and enable, particularly as petabyte-scale data volumes become the norm in our field.

Preface

This book is about the emergence of object storage as a storage technology in the life sciences. As new technology emerges it offers scientists the tools and processes to make advancements in their fields. With these advancements often comes a growing stream of data. Some fields, like genomics, generate more data than others. Within the field of genomics, whole human genome sequencing produces large amounts of unstructured data.

Object storage is built for this kind and quantity of data! Especially when we take into account how the data needs to be handled to ensure its security, accessibility, searchability, and durability. It's not just the data storage and handling that is generating excitement for us. It's also the possibilities that emerge when using an object storage system to facilitate genomic and other scientific advancements. For example, in a clinical setting where turnaround time, reliability, and data mobility are crucial, object storage can be used as a scalable solution for effective clinical genomic data management. Object storage can thus lead to a deeper understanding of how we as humans function and result in medical advancements, such as the ability to personalize drug treatments.

As a technologist, it's easy to get excited about the latest and greatest tech. But that pleasure doesn't compare to the satisfaction of seeing technology being used to solve big, everyday problems. SwiftStack has helped life sciences institutions meet their data management challenges so they can be as effective and impactful as possible. With this book I hope to share with a larger audience what we have learned through deploying object storage for genomics research and bioinformatics. It's a small and largely behind-the-scenes contribution, but it's very gratifying to help clinical and research medicine in their important work.

Meet OpenStack Swift

In the summer of 2010, a revolution came to data center management with the launch of the open-source project OpenStack. One of the initial projects was an object storage system called Swift and it quickly gained large-scale adoption at service providers (including Rackspace, IBM, HP, Internap, NTT, HP, and others) who provide cloud-based storage. Swift allowed organizations to deploy storage infrastructure that is not just API compatible with public cloud storage, but architecturally identical.

The industry had seen how powerful an object storage system could be. Amazon had popularized object storage with their wildly successful Simple Storage Service (S3). However, for data-intensive storage workflows, public cloud can be cost prohibitive and data transfer times can be hard to overcome.

As we will see in upcoming chapters, OpenStack Swift is a new way to think about storage. It isn't a single, monolithic system, but rather a distributed system. OpenStack Swift is a change in how storage works. Swift is a storage system that is purpose-built for 'unstructured' data.

What is Unstructured Data?

Unstructured data is data that does not have a predefined data model and is typically stored as a file rather than as an entry in a database (which would be structured data). The vast majority of new data growth in life sciences is unstructured data with more and more files being generated, as opposed to more rows of data being stored in traditional database environments.

A wide spectrum of companies and institutions are facing greater and greater storage demands. Enterprises are capturing more data, videos, emails, documents, and files of all types.

Meet SwiftStack

SwiftStack is a company that provides highly available and scalable object storage software, based on OpenStack Swift. SwiftStack is a great fit for companies that don't have the dedicated IT resources to install, integrate, and operate Swift directly from source.

Several of the core contributors, who are part of the approval process for code contributions to the Swift repositories, work at SwiftStack. This, in combination with the company's real-world experience in deploying Swift, allows SwiftStack to contribute heavily upstream and lead many of the major initiatives for Swift in collaboration with the rest of the Swift developer community.

The SwiftStack software package includes an unmodified, 100% open source version of OpenStack Swift and adds software components for deployment, integration (with filesystem gateway, authentication and utilization systems), monitoring, and management of Swift clusters. SwiftStack also provides training, consulting, and 24×7 support for SwiftStack software, including Swift.

What's in this Book?

The first three chapters of this book provide a conceptual introduction to the data challenges facing the field of genomics and they introduce object storage - a fundamentally new approach to data storage. Chapter 1 offers a high-level overview of the genomics data avalanche and explains why traditional approaches to storage are not adequate. Chapter 2 explores key genomics use cases in greater detail, examining workflows and data storage needs during sequencing, analysis, and subsequent distribution and collaboration. Next, Chapter 3 focuses on object storage and why it is particularly well-suited to unstructured data.

The following two chapters then present OpenStack Swift and SwiftStack. Chapter 4 focuses on the capabilities of Swift and SwiftStack for working with genomics data. Chapter 5 offers a more general treatment of how OpenStack Swift works.

The final three chapters cover specifics of how to work with SwiftStack. Chapter 6 shows you how to install SwiftStack and create a Swift cluster. Chapter 7 examines some pertinent applications in the context of life sciences that let you access and work with your Swift cluster. Finally, Chapter 8 provides hardware recommendations for SwiftStack deployments.

Conventions Used in this Book

The following typographical conventions are used in this book:

Italic

Indicates new terms, special emphasis, URLs, email addresses, filenames, and extensions.

`Constant width`

Used for program listings, as well as within paragraphs to refer to program elements such as variable or function names, databases, data types, environment variables, statements, and key words.

`Constant width bold`

Shows commands or other text that should be typed literally by the user.

`Constant width italic`

Shows text that should be replaced with user-supplied values or values determined by context.

Using Code Examples

This book aims to help you work effectively with Swift and apply it to genomics use cases. In general, you may use the code in this book in your programs and documentation. You do not need to contact us for permission unless you're reproducing a significant portion of the code. For example, writing a program that uses several chunks of code from this book does not require permission. Selling or distributing a CD-ROM of examples does require permission. Answering a question by citing this book and quoting example code does not require permission. Incorporating a significant amount of example code from this book into your product's documentation does require permission.

We appreciate, but do not require, attribution. An attribution usually includes the title, author, and publication year. For example: "*Object Storage for Genomics: Deploying and Administering OpenStack Swift with SwiftStack for Bioinformatics*, First Edition, by Joe Arnold, Copyright 2015."

If you feel your use of code examples falls outside fair use or the permission given here, feel free to contact us via email (contact@swiftstack.com).

How to Contact Us

SwiftStack is headquartered in San Francisco, California with support operations covering Asian and European timezones. To contact us, you can visit *https://swiftstack.com/contact-us/*. If you have specific questions for me, please email me! You can reach me at joe@swiftstack.com or on Twitter at @joearnold.

We'd Like to Hear From You

As you use this book and work with Swift and SwiftStack, we invite your comments and feedback. From the very start, Swift has benefited from the contributions of hundreds of developers and users. And we hope that doesn't stop, particularly as we work to deepen our field specific expertise in genomics data management. This book is our first attempt to synthesize this material; we'd love to hear your ideas for making it better (and our sincerst apologies if there are any errors).

We invite your comments, feedback, and suggestions. Please let us know what we need to correct or add; share your insights; and help us create a resource that will serve you better. You can do so by visiting http://swiftstack.com/books/Object-Storage-for-Genomics.

Acknowledgements

Many thanks to our customers and supporters in life sciences for allowing us to work closely with them so that we could gain an understanding of their storage challenges.

I'm very appreciative to Chris Dagdigian of BioTeam for setting the stage in the Foreword of this book. I would like to thank the folks at

BioTeam including Anushka Brownley, Simon Twigger, Bhanu Rekepalli for their insightful questions. Many thanks to Dirk Peterson of Fred Hutchinson Cancer Research Center who has been providing feedback to SwiftStack for years. Additional thanks to Peyton McNully, Andy Crouse, and Brandon Kruse of HudsonAlpha Institute for Biotechnology for sharing their storage challenges.

There are over a hundred developers who have contributed to Swift. I'd like to thank each one of them for their ongoing contributions. There are also hundreds of operators of Swift who count on a stable, reliable storage system. Without them, Swift would just be an interesting idea. So, I would like to thank all of the Swift operators for trusting us with your data.

This book couldn't have come together without the support of a large cast. Everyone at SwiftStack in some way has contributed to writing this book. I'd like to especially thank Chris Nelson and Doug Soltesz for connecting the challenges faced by life sciences to a SwiftStack solution; I'd like to thank Amanda Plimpton who has kept this publication on track. Much appreciation to Mark Guthridge for his visual guidance and Mark Feldman of Writing Works for advocating for the reader.

Conclusion

Thanks to advances in genomics technology there is a growing need to store and distribute large amounts of data. Swift was designed for doing just that and has been adopted as a storage standard in many industries. Here at SwiftStack we have also learned much from our real-world deployments, geared specifically for genomics, at research institutions. We truly believe in the mission of these research organizations that Swift has helped.

This book aims to share information and our experiences with you, the IT providers in life sciences, to help you solve these new storage challenges quickly and easily, making your successful conversion to Swift, well … swifter.

## Chapter One

Introduction

Data Challenges for Genomics Research

Technology Drives Discovery

We are in an era of genomics research in which technology is driving discovery. The initial obstacle to better human genomic understanding was sequencing the human genome. After several generations of sequencing technology, we have the ability to translate genomes into data. Now the challenge is processing, analyzing, and distributing all this data.

From Theory to Practice

Next-generation genome sequencers are enabling new use cases. As the price of sequencing goes down, genomic sequencing is spreading far beyond traditional discovery-oriented use cases in the lab. Genomic sequencing is now used in clinical and diagnostic use cases as well as in developing personalized treatments for individual patients.

Generating and using such sequencing requires compute power, storage, and availability. For example, one Illumina HiSeq X Ten can generate 130 TB of raw sequence data each month. Raw data is not useful until it is consolidated, aligned, and packaged, all of which further increases storage requirements. Automated pipelines and human researchers working on instrument-generated data will commonly increase the "derived" or "downstream" data by a factor of 2 or 3. Hundreds of dedicated compute cores constantly access the data to assemble institutionally useful files and ultimately generate a finished product of a genome sequence and possibly a variant analysis. Distribution of the files and finished product provides the real time access to thousands of genomes that makes future research breakthroughs possible.

Next Generation Technologies

With next-generation genomic sequencing comes the need for the next generation in storage technology. With sequencing costs driven down an order-of-magnitude, more sequences than ever before are being generated and they need to be stored and processed, creating a storage cost bottleneck.

Additionally, as the amount of data has increased, its access patterns have also intensified. As this sequencing data becomes more important in clinical contexts, processing times become more of an issue. What used to take days, will now need to be done in hours.

Example Genomic Services Laboratory Workflow

A single genomics laboratory can generate over ¼ petabyte of data per month! Here's how:

- A HiSeq X Ten cluster produces 13TB (20 million files) of sequence data every 3 days (or roughly 10 times a month)
- Sequence data is moved to storage cluster and converted to FASTQ, generating 8TB of data every 3 days
- Aligning and compressing FASTQ to BAM generates an additional 2TB of data every 3 days

- Distributing BAM to research groups and clinics (2 download sites) generates another 4TB of data every 3 days

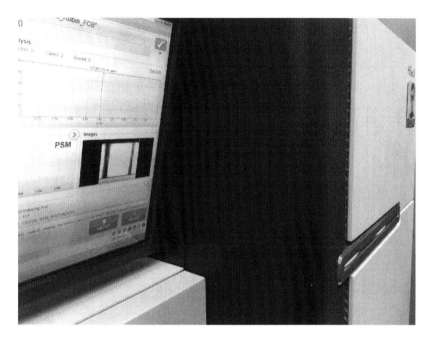

Illumina HiSeq X Figure 1-1

Overcoming the Data Avalanche

As the data volume increases, there are new problems to be solved.

Turnover Time

The ability to process more data more quickly is a big challenge. Hundreds of thousands of base call files need to be processed rapidly. Reducing variant analysis time in a clinical context means faster diagnoses for patients.

Data lacks metadata / "search-ability"

More data means more projects and files to track. Data proliferates without the ability to search and track it. Either storage systems grow without bounds, or data is lost on shelves of USB drives.

Staff don't clean up system data

Data continues to proliferate. As projects wind down, or data is consolidated it is important to have processes to consolidate and remove unneeded files. It is never appropriate for IT staff to make data deletion or curation decisions on their own. Data management and lifecycle policies need to be agreed upon with the direct participation of the data owners, consumers, and producers.

What is the cost of a data hiccup?

As production times come down, the cost of storage downtime unavailability goes up. Storage upgrades shouldn't take down lab production. Lab downtime is costly, delaying runs and necessitating resequencing. Furthermore, additional reagents, required for reprocessing, are a substantial added expense.

Continuously feeding HPC systems

Downtime spans further than an interface with a sequencer. Increasingly, genomics research combines the technical elements of sequencing with high-performance computing (HPC). In that context, availability, reliability, and performance of the storage systems are extremely important. As the storage footprint increases, interrupting jobs in an HPC cluster can become very disruptive.

Multiple generations of hardware

Storage growth happens over time and multiple generations of hardware are often represented to the organization as separate storage systems. This requires bioinformaticists and researchers to have a complete understanding of what data goes where. Ideally, new storage systems integrate with the previous generation into a single storage environment

Data growth similar to a Fortune 500 company, with 1/10 the IT team and budget

Life sciences and genomics institutions typically generate as much data as a Fortune 500 company. But they typically have only a fraction of the IT staff and budget. Finding cost-effective solutions for grant-driven and/or nonprofit institutions requires re-thinking data storage.

Storage & infrastructure as an after-thought

Most bio IT professionals have a few war stories involving terabyte-class data producing instruments showing up on campus or in a lab with zero notice or advance communication with IT, storage, compute, or infrastructure groups. It is very common to see the following:

- Instrument sales teams downplay infrastructure requirements to make the sale or they offer data management suggestions ("Cloud!", "Local Appliance!") that are wildly at odds with organizational policy.
- Pre-sale site surveys do not fully examine what kind of net working , bandwidth, and infrastructure support can be extended directly to the instrument. This results in brittle environments, failed experiments, and angry staff.
- Instrument purchasers often spend 100% of their budget on the platform itself plus reagent kits and lab techs to operate the system. Little thought and even less money is left to support data ingest, analysis, and long term online, nearline, and archival storage.

Traditional Storage is not the Answer

Traditional storage is not the answer to this increase in life sciences data. Current storage architectures have bottlenecks and limitations, particularly with an influx of many small files. Genomics sequencer clusters can generate millions of files over a short period of time.

Life sciences IT teams were some of the first to adopt network-attached storage (NAS). Researchers needed concurrent shared access in an easy to consume way. The initial storage systems based on direct-attached storage, or storage-area networks prevented shared access and were not convenient for unstructured data.

As the use of NAS grew, life sciences teams hit some of the early bottlenecks. These NAS systems were typically constrained by the capabilities of a single system – for example its number of networking ports and disk drives.

From this, a new generation of clustered-NAS emerged. Companies like Panasis, Isilon, and Bluearc expanded the boundaries of traditional NAS architectures. However, fundamental limitations existed on the cluster size, the number of controllers, and the amount of capacity that can be managed as a single cluster. Even this newer class of scale-out NAS architectures can have difficulties dealing with current life sciences demands.

Multiple Petabytes

Many NAS solutions are not engineered for seamless and non-disruptive growth into a very large single-namespace. To accommodate these large-scale needs, multiple storage systems are often deployed within the same organization.

Increasingly, scale-out NAS products have become a popular choice in life sciences environments as they can deliver massive multiple-petabyte, single-namespace capability with reasonable operational overhead. These systems have their own functional and operational tradeoffs. As the system scales, more coordination and internal "housekeeping" must be done across multiple elements in order to maintain consistency and high availability across the namespace. This becomes increasingly problematic at large scale, particularly for use cases and access patterns where lots of small files are involved.

Multiple Namespaces

Having multiple pools of storage increases the complexity of management for IT staff. This not only includes day-to-day operations, but it also includes informing research staff what each storage pool should be used for.

Each new namespace (*"/data1"*, *"/data2"*, *"/data3"*, etc.) creates a new "island" of data and as islands proliferate so do issues with management, curation, version control, and data provenance. End-users are often not motivated to directly curate, manage, and cull their files so each new island represents a non-trivial data management problem.

As a result, data can be duplicated from one system to another resulting in wasted space. It can get confusing for users who have to grapple with which systems they should be using and which is the latest copy of their data.

The financial and operational costs of these inefficient practices become extraordinarily significant at petabyte-scale. A few terabytes of duplicate or wasted data is no big deal but a petabyte of duplicated or non-essential data can represent more than $1 Million USD in wasted capital.

Cost

Price is also a consideration. The price per usable terabyte varies widely from $250/TB up to $10,000/TB depending on the vendor.

Keeping pace with high-density drives

New, high-capacity hard drives are becoming available. As 8, 10, and 12 terabyte drives come onto the market, these larger drives represent bigger failure domains. Longer rebuild times increase the risk of data loss. In a RAID system, rebuilds need to be performed while the system is still servicing storage requests which can increase stress on the system.

Unsecured and unprotected external USB storage units on laboratory benchtop. Source: Chris Dagdigian, BioTeam. Used with permission.
Figure 1-2

The High Cost of Getting It Wrong

Scientists and lab staff are smart, motivated, natural problem solvers. Any organization that fails to address instrument data storage requirements will find themselves bypassed by end-users who will apply creative solutions to the problem. The solutions may violate internal policy (cloud storage, etc.) or fail to adequately address issues of data integrity, safety, confidentiality, or backup/archive.

The financial, legal, and operational cost of getting this wrong can be very significant for any organization

Conclusion

In this chapter we examined the challenges that organizations face as genomics data increases dramatically. With the cost of sequencing dropping, more and more data is being generated. Data needs and access patterns are also changing as sequencing is now used in clinical contexts which require shorter turnaround times. Labs and research organizations often invest in data intensive instruments without sufficient planning and budget to deal with the new data. IT teams too often find themselves with disparate pools of storage that are confusing for everyone and that lack searchable metadata. Object storage, which is the focus of the following chapter, is the best solution to the many data management challenges facing life sciences organizations.

Chapter Two

Genomics Use Cases with Object Storage

There are two genomics use cases that can take advantage of object storage. First is the storage of data produced during sequencing and subsequent analysis. Second is as a repository for the long-term storage of large amounts of data. The data in the repository can feed into high-performance compute environments for analysis. This provides a long-term, low-cost, durable archive that can be distributed across multiple, geographically dispersed data centers.

In this chapter we cover typical workflows for genomics sequencing, analysis, and data storage. For each of these we examine the particular data demands and explain how object storage through OpenStack Swift and SwiftStack meets those demands.

Storage for Sequencing Workflow

Every living organism has a genome that can be sequenced. During the sequencing process there are various storage and compute workflows that are used in order to generate a genome sequence. In this section we will cover the data that is generated during this process using Illumina sequencing instruments.

Sequencing

Through a chemical and photographic process, Illumina sequencers analyze prepared genetic material on flow cells. Each lane is further subdivided and scanned multiple times.

This is where the first storage challenge comes in. With a fully-running set of 10 Illumina HiSeq X sequencers, 4.6 million BCL files are generated in a three day sequencing run. There are also millions of additional files and thumbnails all of which are required for processing. The HiSeq X Ten System produces up to 13TB across 20 million files over this three day period.

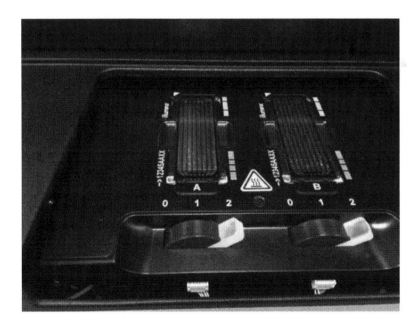

Flow cells on an Illumina HiSeq X Figure 2-1

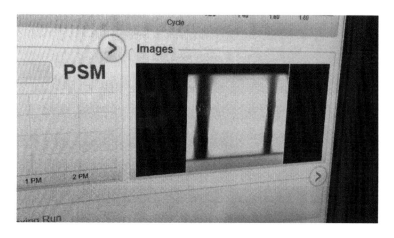

Thumbnail image from an Illumina HiSeq X Figure 2-2

This process requires the following storage characteristics:

Small-file ingest

The storage system needs to be able to distribute files across a large number of individual storage devices (drives). This allows many drives to participate in the data ingest, increasing the throughput capability of the storage system.

OpenStack Swift / SwiftStack is architected to distribute data across many devices in a storage cluster, which provides high throughput ingest of lots of small files over the course of multiple, back-to-back sequencing runs.

Highly durable write

As data is streaming from multiple sequencers, the storage system must be able to support a continuous ingest rate. Ideally, writes should be placed in a primary durable storage location.

A write is fully durable to its primary locations with OpenStack Swift / SwiftStack. Either with multiple replicas or erasure codes, when a write is acknowledged, a durable write is complete.

Integration

The workstation attached to a sequencer will either speak native object storage, or will present a filesystem (CIFS) mount point.

OpenStack Swift / SwiftStack will integrate directly with native object storage device, while a CIFS filesystem mount point would require other methods. SwiftStack provides a Filesystem Gateway which is additional capability beyond OpenStack Swift.

Raw Data Processing

The next stage is consolidating the BCL data into a FASTQ file. A compute cluster or large server is used for this processing. A typical FASTQ is a data file containing all sequence reads from a given instrument run. It summarizes the individual base calls and their associated quality scores for each read.

This process requires the following storage characteristics:

High Throughput, Small File Read

Each node in the compute cluster will be reading different sections of BCL files. This can place a lot of strain on a traditional file-based storage system. While some workloads can benefit from caching, this workload cannot. Each read into the storage system is for unique data.

OpenStack Swift / SwiftStack scales horizontally for read requests. Read requests are distributed across the system, increasing performance.

Genome Assembly/Alignment

The next operation is to map the reads in the FASTQ files to positions in the reference genome sequence. During the alignment processing DNA sequences from the FASTQ files are aligned to the best-matching positions in the reference genome.

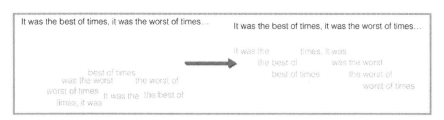

The alignment process organizes sequence data Figure 2-3

In the first step, software running in a compute cluster will generate an index of the FASTQ. This indexing process can be multi-threaded. The second step is the alignment process itself, which is single-threaded, but can be hardware accelerated.

The output of this process is a SAM file with aligned sequence data and metadata. SAM stands for Sequence Alignment Map and is a text file. This SAM file is compressed into binary format, BAM (Binary Alignment Map). This multi-GB file is frequently stored, since it contains not just all sequence, quality, and position information but is also the product of significant computational steps that one might not want to repeat.

This process requires the following storage characteristics:

Large File Storage

Final output of the process is a large file. Large files if stored sequentially can take a long time to write and read from a storage system.

OpenStack Swift / SwiftStack supports large-file format that chunks up objects into smaller segments making it possible to quickly load data in parallel.

Variant Calling

SAM files are around 400GB for a whole human genome, and BAM files around 150GB, depending on percentage of coverage and depth of coverage. The percentage of coverage refers to how much of the reference genome was mapped. The depth of coverage is an average that describes how many times that given part of the genome was sequenced. The above numbers represent 30x coverage. Clinical sequencing of whole genomes may end up being 2-3 times deeper than research grade genomes which means 2-3 times more data. Sequencing of DNA from tissues made up of mixtures of cells (e.g. cancer and normal tissue, in a tumor) may be even deeper, to identify subpopulations with important variants.

In the variant calling step the BAM file is analyzed to find differences or variants, between the sample genome that was sequenced and the reference genome that the sample genome was aligned against. The most common kind of difference is a single nucleotide or base difference between the sample and reference, and these are called single nucleotide polymorphisms (SNPs). The entire set of variants are written to a file in a format called variant call format (VCF).

This process requires the following storage characteristics:

High Throughput, Large File Upload and Download

These are large input files which benefit from parallel uploads and downloads for very fast transfer times. The files can be transferred into dedicated compute clusters for variant detection and visualization using BAM file viewers.

SwiftStack supports a standard method to upload a single file via multiple chunks. These chunks can also be used to do a multi-threaded download of large objects so that they can be quickly transferred.

Distribution and Collaboration

Researchers use genomics data to collaborate across institutions. Researchers and clinicians need methods to get this data that are efficient, secure, fast, and compatible with their workflow.

Some of the biggest advantages of object storage over NAS are in how it deals with large files. With object storage, the parallel upload and download of large files is a huge benefit to distribution and collaboration. Distribution and collaboration require the following storage characteristics:

Multi-Region

With large genomic datasets there are throughput benefits to having that data nearby (network-speaking, that is). Data on high speed networks means more data can be analyzed more quickly and data can be distributed more quickly.

SwiftStack provides multi-data center support within a single storage cluster. Additionally, there is the ability to create storage policies so that data placement can be fully controlled.

Authenticated Access

When multiple institutions collaborate, or when data is being sent to other researchers or clinicians, it's important to have authenticated access for the data.

SwiftStack supports integration with external authentication systems such as Active Directory and LDAP and it has an administrative console for user management. SwiftStack will also track how much data each account is storing and downloading.

Multiple Download Methods

Multiple methods are sometimes required for transferring files and not every consumer of the data is on the local-area network. Here, web-based download tools which can provide authenticated access are useful. Additionally, desktop or server tools which work over wide-area networks can be very useful.

SwiftStack provides a web-based file browser to make it easy for desktop users to download files. There are also a wide-variety of desktop-based tools, a command-line client for servers, and client libraries for developers.

Rich Metadata

Often the distribution process is initiated by a LIMS (Laboratory Information Management System) or other project workflow management system. Metadata related to the files can be stored with the file itself, which can then be used by the LIMS.

OpenStack Swift / SwiftStack can store metadata associated with each object. Additionally, middleware can be installed to index metadata in a queryable database.

Genetic Material to Variant Processing Turnaround Time

Finding differences between the sample genome and either the reference genome or other individuals is one of the promises of genomics. This lets us isolate what makes individuals different from each other and other species and lets us recognize mutations such as cancer.

The faster we are able to compare genomes, the faster scientific research can happen, the faster a clinician can get results, and the faster a patient can get a diagnosis. Speed is critical for clinical applications in a genomics workflow.

Storage needs to enable a compute cluster to run at "full-tilt." As more data is generated, more data needs to be processed. Rather than performing jobs on single workstations, compute clusters need to be fed at high data rate

SwiftStack scales-out to support the scale of a compute cluster. High throughput rates means less idle CPU time waiting for data to arrive. This enables the use of a compute cluster, shortening the processing time.

Personal Genomics

A person has roughly 3-4 million SNPs and a few thousand structural variants. In addition, in cancer genomics, the cancer cells have their own set of variants that differ from a patient's genome. Knowing what cancer cell-specific variants a patient has allows the doctor to personalize that patient's drug treatment.

The reduction in sequencing cost makes such personalized treatments more feasible. Now the compute, storage, and delivery costs need to drop commensurately.

SwiftStack is compatible with standard, x86 server components, directly writing to disks rather than to expensive storage appliances. This dramatically reduces the cost of storage and provides the flexibility to buy what is needed, when it's needed.

Storage Archive

Whether you control the end-to-end data flow, or you are providing IT services, a lower-cost storage target will allow IT dollars to be extended.

Multi-Tenant Chargeback

Institutions are adopting a chargeback model to incentivize more economical storage practices. This has enabled them to introduce object storage as an appealing lower-cost storage solution. Even with plenty of warning, users tend not to change their behavior until they are faced with the real costs of data storage.

SwiftStack provides storage utilization information via reports or an API to track how much each account is utilizing. At Fred Hutchinson Cancer Research Center, starting storage chargebacks triggered immediate data movement, migrating over 30 TB per day. This orderly migration turned into a flood when researchers realized how much they could save by using SwiftStack.

Variety of Access Methods

When a storage system is being used for live archive, it helps to have multiple ways to access the storage system.

Fred Hutchinson Cancer Research Center portal for department chargeback Figure 2-4

SwiftStack can serve as a back-end storage target for workflow managers such as Galaxy, a backup storage target for applications such as CommVault, as well as provide desktop file collaboration tools, in addition to a Filesystem Gateway for CIFS/NFS access.

High Aggregate Throughput

When rolling out a multi-tenant storage cluster, high aggregate throughput is required, since multiple systems and users will be streaming data in parallel, often into HPC clusters.

SwiftStack is ideal for multi-tenant genomics use cases. In a moderate-size cluster, a 25GB genome file can be loaded to tier 1 storage in 10 seconds. This is possible with many parallel streams, which maximize throughput - ideal for HPC cluster architecture.

Conclusion

The emergence of next-generation sequencers has dramatically increased data production rates. Because of this change, a need has arisen for lower cost storage that can both support the output of next-generation sequencers and meet the availability needs of high-performance computing (HPC) clusters.

Object storage is well suited to these genomics data storage needs. In the next chapter, we will further discuss how storage is changing and where OpenStack Swift and SwiftStack fit in the storage landscape.

## Chapter Three

Why Object Storage?

The majority of genomics research data is 'unstructured' data. This means that the data does not have a pre-defined data model and is typically stored as a file rather than as an entry in a database (which would be structured data.) In this chapter, we will briefly discuss the requirements and tradeoffs of various strategies for storing unstructured data. We will then examine object storage, which is best suited to storing unstructured data, particularly through the storage architecture known as Software-Defined Storage (SDS).

Requirements for Storing Unstructured Data

Storage of unstructured data needs to ensure durability, availability , low cost, and manageability.

Durability

The cost of producing data is high and sometimes data cannot be reproduced. So ensuring the integrity and availability of data (durability) is extremely important. It's often a requirement to have data protected in multiple locations to provide some measure of durability.

Availability

Very often unstructured data needs to be available in an instant with high aggregate throughput. While some data can be archived, researchers expect most of their data to be reliably available.

Low Cost

Unstructured data needs to be stored at low cost. With enough money, any storage problem can be solved. However, we live in a world of constraints. Available budgets necessitate low cost data storage solutions.

Manageability

With larger storage systems coming online, manageability becomes critical. It is common for a small number of administrators to support a large number of storage servers. This is only possible with well designed, simple to use management tools.

Why Filesystems are Not Enough

While it would be ideal if there was a one-size-fits-all solution for storage needs, there isn't. Storage systems entail tradeoffs that we can think of as responses to their particular requirements and circumstances. The CAP-theorem, first advanced by Eric Brewster (UC Berkeley, Computer Science) in 2000 succinctly frames the problem. It states that distributed computer systems cannot simultaneously provide consistency, availability, and partition tolerance. This means that you're left to choose the two that are most important for your particular circumstances. (This principle is similar to the adage that says you can only pick two: fast, cheap, or good.)

If the system needs consistency (for example when you're a bank recording account balances), then either availability or partition tolerance would need to suffer. This is typically what is needed for transactional workloads such as supporting databases. However if you want availability and partition tolerance, then you need to tolerate your system being occasionally inconsistent.

The bottom line is that it's impossible to build a system that can deliver all three: consistency, availability, and partition tolerance. Purpose-built storage systems will, however, offer greater reliability for a particular workload than a general-purpose storage system designed to support all workloads.

Swift demonstrates this in its handling of the workloads required for large amounts of unstructured data. Following the CAP-theorem, Swift sacrifices consistency to gain availability and partition tolerance. This allows Swift to be very durable and highly available

Object Storage Compared with Other Storage Types

Different types of data have different access patterns and therefore can be best stored on different types of storage systems. There are three broad categories of data storage: block storage, file storage, and object storage.

Block Storage

This stores structured data, which is represented as equal-size blocks (say, 212 bits per block) without putting any interpretation on the bits. Often, this kind of storage is useful when the application needs to tightly control the structure of the data. A common use for block storage is databases, which can use a raw block device to efficiently read and write structured data. Additionally, filesystems are used to abstract a block device, which then does everything from running operating systems to storing files.

File Storage

This is what we're most used to seeing as desktop users. In its simplest form, file storage takes a hard drive (like the one on your computer) and exposes a filesystem on it for storing unstructured data. You see the filesystem when you open and close documents on your computer. A data center contains systems that expose a filesystem over a network. Although file storage provides a useful abstraction on top of a storage device, there are challenges as the system scales. File storage needs strong consistency, which creates constraints as the system grows and is put under high demand. In addition, filesystems often require other features (such as file locking) that make them not suited to working with large amounts of data.

Object Storage

This will be familiar to those who regularly access the Internet or use mobile devices. Object storage doesn't provide access to raw blocks of data; nor does it offer file-based access. Instead, it provides access to whole objects or blobs of data—generally through an API specific to that system. Objects are accessible via URLs using HTTP protocols, similar to how websites are accessible in web browsers. Object storage abstracts these locations as URLs so that the storage system can grow and scale independently from the underlying storage mechanisms. This makes object storage ideal for systems that need to grow and scale for capacity, concurrency, or both.

One of the main advantages of object storage is its ability to distribute requests for objects across a large number of storage servers. This provides reliable, scalable storage for large amounts of data at a relatively low cost.

As the system scales, it can continue to present a single namespace. This means an application or user doesn't need to—and some would say shouldn't—know which part of the storage system is going to be used. This reduces operator burden, unlike a filesystem where operators might have to manage multiple storage volumes. Because an object storage system provides a single namespace, there is no need to break data up and send it to different storage locations, which can increase complexity and confusion.

A New Storage Architecture: Software-Defined Storage

The history of data storage began with hard drives connected to a mainframe. Then storage migrated off the mainframe to separate, dedicated storage systems with in-line controllers. However, the world keeps changing. Applications are now much larger. This means that their storage needs have pushed beyond what the architecture of an in-line storage controller can accommodate.

Older generations of storage often ran on custom hardware and used closed software. Typically, there were expensive maintenance contracts, difficult data migration, and a tightly controlled ecosystem. These systems needed tight controls to predict and prevent failures.

The scale of unstructured data storage is forcing a sea change in storage architecture, and this is where Software-Defined Storage (SDS) enters our story. It represents a huge shift in how data is stored. With SDS, the entire storage stack is recast to best meet the criteria of durability, availability, low cost, and manageability.

It is key for an SDS system to be able to effectively manage scale and drive operational efficiencies in the infrastructure. Capacity management is much simpler with an SDS system, because each component is part of a distributed system, so upgrades, expansions, and decommissions can be achieved without any downtime and with no need for 'forklift' data migration.

There is no application sharing or managing volumes which can drive operational knowledge and complexity into applications because the SDS system is one cohesive system. Users do not need to ask for or know 'which storage pool' should be used because there is only one namespace.

The separation of physical hardware from the software allows for mix and match hardware configurations within the same storage system. Drives of varying capacity, or even CPU capability can be used in the same system. One benefit of this is that capacity increments can be more incremental. This allows for just-in-time purchasing and lets you take advantage of the technology innovation curve.

Why OpenStack Swift with SwiftStack?

SwiftStack is an object storage system, which, as we have discussed, means it trades immediate consistency for eventual consistency. This allows SwiftStack to achieve high availability, redundancy, throughput, and capacity. With a focus on availability over consistency, SwiftStack has no transaction or locking delays. Large numbers of simultaneous reads are fast, as are simultaneous writes. This means that SwiftStack is capable of scaling to an extremely large number of concurrent connections and extremely large sets of data. SwiftStack uses OpenStack Swift, an open source project, that has gained a community of hundreds of contributors. Since its launch it has gotten even more stable, become faster, and added many great new features. SwiftStack is the leader in OpenStack Swift and has simplified management and deployment. SwiftStack also provides access methods such as CIFS/NFS in addition to the HTTP API.

SwiftStack can also be installed on standard server hardware. This means that low-cost server components can be used to build the storage system. By relying on SwiftStack to provide the logical software management of data rather than specialized vendor-specific hardware, you gain incredible flexibility in the features, deployment, and scaling of your storage system. This, in essence, is what software-defined storage is all about.

But what might be most interesting is what happens "under the hood." OpenStack Swift and SwiftStack are a fundamentally new sort of storage system. This system isn't single and monolithic, but rather it's a distributed system that easily scales out and tolerates failure without compromising data availability.

This comes with some constraints, to be sure, but SwiftStack and OpenStack Swift are a perfect match for the data needs of genetics research. OpenStack Swift is more and more widespread and is evolving into a standard way to store and distribute large amounts of data in this field.

Conclusion

A major change in storage has occurred with the emergence of object storage and software-defined storage systems. This enables large, distributed storage systems to be built with standards-based storage servers. Software-defined storage has dramatically reduced the costs of deploying data-intensive applications, as there is no need for individual hardware components to be durable.

In the next chapter we introduce the specific capabilities of OpenStack Swift and SwiftStack which are particularly useful for genomics.

## Chapter Four

Swift and SwiftStack
Capabilities Overview for Genomics

Beyond Swift's core functionality to store and serve data durably at large scale, Swift and SwiftStack have many features of particular benefit to genomics research.

Genomics research combines the technical elements of sequencing with high-performance computing (HPC). In that context, availability and reliability are extremely important.

Modern NAS and scale-out NAS are reliable, however they cannot be fully trusted to sustain a major OS upgrade or capacity addition without hiccups. Therefore, maintenance windows are reluctantly scheduled and HPC jobs are paused to play it safe. Users are extremely disappointed when jobs run for days and are then interrupted at the 11th hour!

Sequencing is moving from research (low reliability accepted in turn for cutting edge technology and low cost) to the clinic where uptime and time predictability are most critical. Given this the specific capabilities of OpenStack Swift and SwiftStack - the central subject of this chapter - are especially useful.

SwiftStack Capabilities for Genomics

SwiftStack is an object storage system which includes an unmodified, 100% open-source release of OpenStack Swift at the core. In this section, we will provide a brief overview of SwiftStack and cover additional capabilities.

SwiftStack Overview

In addition to Swift, SwiftStack provides extensive functionality for deploying, integrating, upgrading, and managing single and multi-region Swift clusters coupled with enterprise support. SwiftStack object storage software is licensed separately and provides the following functionality above and beyond core Swift:

- Swift cluster management and configuration
- Automated install process
- Drive inventory management
- Gradual capacity adjustment
- Multi-data center and global cluster management
- Capacity management
- No downtime, rolling upgrades
- LDAP and Active Directory integration
- Utilization API

A key characteristic of SwiftStack is that it decouples the control, management, and configuration of the Swift storage nodes from the physical hardware. Although the actual storage services run on the servers where Swift is installed,deployment, management, and monitoring are conducted out-of-band by a separate storage controller, which can manage one or more clusters.

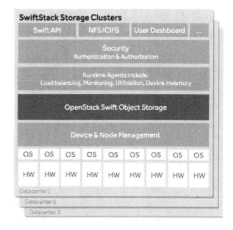

Components of SwiftStack Figure 4-1

This approach has many benefits because operators can now manage multiple, geographically distributed storage clusters from a single management system; dynamically tune clusters to optimize performance; respond to hardware failures; and upgrade clusters while they are still running. All of these capacities are driven programmatically for the entire storage tier, independent of where the storage resources are deployed.

The following capabilities will be of particular interest to genomics IT teams.

Multi-Region Management

SwiftStack provides a simple way to deploy, configure, and manage nodes across multiple regions and data centers. Swift organizes storage nodes by zones, regions, and possibly storage policies. Regions are a way to define parts of a cluster that are physically separate; most often this is geographic (regional). Within a region, the cluster can further be grouped into zones. Zones are generally created to help identify the failure points (e.g. all the nodes in one rack or all the nodes in one datacenter) so that the copies of the data can be placed in different

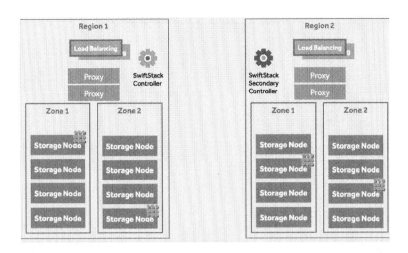

A two region SwiftStack cluster configured with a four replica storage policy Figure 4-2

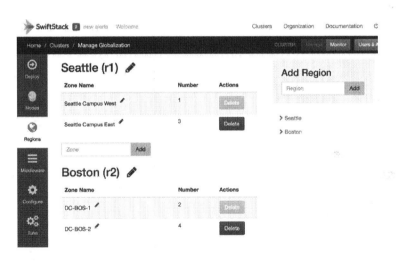

Multi-Region & zone management with SwiftStack Controller Figure 4-3

zones and regions to isolate failures and ensure the durability and accessibility of the data in the cluster. We'll get into storage policies, which allow various data protection strategies, shortly but first the example below offers a look at how a two region cluster with two zones per region might store four copies of one object as far from each other as possible in separate regions and zones. This shows how the object would still be available even if a zone (e.g. top of rack switch dies) or region (e.g. city-wide power outage) was temporarily unavailable

A two region SwiftStack cluster configured with a four replica storage policy

In the life sciences, multiple regions would be useful for two reasons – data protection and data distribution. When a second region is used for data protection, fewer proxy nodes need to be deployed. When a second region is used for data distribution, storage requests can be routed to nearby data, improving latency and reducing network congestion.

SwiftStack makes configuration of regions and zones in a cluster simple by providing operators with a web interface that easily allows the addition and removal of regions and zones.

Storage Policy Management

While regions and zones serve as a way to organize nodes, storage policies are used in Swift as a way to organize and manage objects. This is done by applying storage policies to containers which hold objects. One policy is applied to one container and then all objects placed in it will be handled according to that policy. The policy is affecting the objects so they are object storage policies but are commonly referred to as storage policies.

The default configuration of a Swift cluster will have all nodes available for storage and a default object storage policy applied automatically to containers. This default policy says that objects should be copied so that a total of three copies will be saved across the cluster. Custom storage policies are created when you want objects to be stored differently. For example if the objects will only be stored on a subset of nodes (e.g. only the ones with SSDs) or if a different number of copies of the data should be stored (e.g. like the four copies we showed in the example above). ,

Storage policies allow objects to be stored based on the following criteria:

1. Data protection strategy: number of replicas or erasure code strategy

2. Performance of drives
3. Geographical location (region / zone)
4. Efficient data placement based on projected ring size

Example Use Cases

Swift's configuration options allow a great deal of flexibility in how data is stored in the cluster. Different options work better for different use cases. A benefit of using storage policies is that a single Swift deployment can offer multiple data storage options at the same time - allowing it to best serve multiple use cases. These use cases cover some common scenarios for life sciences data.

Reduced Redundancy

Use Case: Lots of data is written but less frequently read. Errors on upload will be retried.

Number of Replicas: 2

Highly Scalable Flat Storage (Standard, 3-Replica)

Use Case: Large variety of files and access patterns. Availability and simplicity is most important.

Number of Replicas: 3

High Performance Storage

Use Case: Many small objects accessed frequently.

Number of Replicas: 3-5

Highly Available Geo-Distributed

Use Case: Data is created and accessed in multiple geo-distributed regions. A failure at one site should not disrupt access to storage in another.

Number of Replicas: 2 per region

Region Local Storage

Use Case: Data is only created and accessed from a single site. Access to data from another region should be rare with

Manage Policies for Cluster

Name	Devices	Part Power	Replicas	
Account & Container	0	16	3	Edit

Object Policies

Name	Storage Policy Index	Devices	Part Power	Replicas	Default	Deprecated		
Standard-Replica	0	10	16	3	⊙		Edit	
ReducedRedundancy	1	10	16	2			Edit	
HighPerformanceStorage	2	10	16	5			Edit	
RegionLocalStorage	3	5	16	3			Edit	

Create Storage Policy

Submit

Storage Policy Management with SwiftStack 4-4

an expectation of higher latency or reduced availability due to network interruption.

Number of Replicas: 2-3 in a single region

Archive Store

Use Case: Data is stored and retrieved for archival purposes.

Use erasure coding storage policy rather than replicas.

Multi-generation Hardware Support

SwiftStack can incorporate multiple generations of storage hardware within the same storage cluster. This lowers total cost of ownership (TCO) because IT teams can get the most out of capital investments by selecting the most cost effective hardware each time their storage needs increase.

This flexibility reduces vendor lock-in, which in turn promotes alternative sourcing for upgrades and capacity expansions. It allows you to turn a multitude of disparate hardware, which is all too frequently what research organizations have, into a cohesive storage system.

Beyond capacity additions, SwiftStack enables better management of hardware lifecycles especially as older equipment is replaced with denser, lower power equipment. With SwiftStack, hardware end-of-life doesn't mean forklift upgrade. Instead, hardware can be replaced incrementally. This allows you to take advantage of the hardware upgrade cycle where performance/capacity to price ratios are continuously going up.

Data Placement

By default, SwiftStack places data in cluster locations that are "as unique-as-possible." This lets Swift intelligently place data on any storage device in the cluster, preferring locations that are in different zones, nodes, and drives. All data stored in SwiftStack also has "handoff" locations defined, which are alternative data placement locations in the cluster should one of the copies not be available due to a hardware failure.

Swift tries to evenly distribute data across all the devices (drives) and nodes in the system. Swift uses a consistent hashing ring to pseudo-randomly distribute all copies of an object across the drives in the cluster according to the size of each. While Swift tries to respect the relative sizes of different disks, it is inevitable that smaller disks or disks that are part of multiple storage policies will fill up faster. As with any storage system, it's important for an operator to pay attention to the space on the drives to make sure that they're not getting too full. A good rule of thumb is to keep the cluster at least 10-20% free, so that there is enough time to order new hardware.

Because Swift stores data essentially level across everything, if the cluster is 80% full and you're adding a new node or a new rack that's 0% full, it has to redistribute the data so that it levels across all nodes (new and old). Once complete, the newly leveled cluster will be at a lower percentage of fullness. If you add the new drives all at once, there will be a lot of data moving in your network which could (very likely) have a negative impact on the performance of the cluster. Adding the new drives gradually is the better way to go.

Gradual Capacity Adjustment

When adding new capacity, you usually don't add just one hard drive! It is more typical to add a new server with many drives or a rack filled with servers. That's a pretty good chunk of data capacity. Swift has built-in capabilities that let administrators control the addition of capacity to a cluster, to prevent network bottlenecks and ensure that data is not left vulnerable during large capacity changes.

SwiftStack takes it a step further and automates the process so that administrators do not need to calculate and kick off round after round of gradual adjustments. Instead, the SwiftStack Controller automates the process of adding capacity, e.g. new drives or new nodes, to a Swift cluster. Administrators would use the web interface to either add the new resources immediately or gradually.

Adding capacity immediately, using the "Add Now" button, means that the SwiftStack Controller will add the full capacity of the new cluster resources right away, which increases the replication traffic as it evenly redistributes the data across the cluster. As we have pointed out this has the potential to create network bottlenecks.

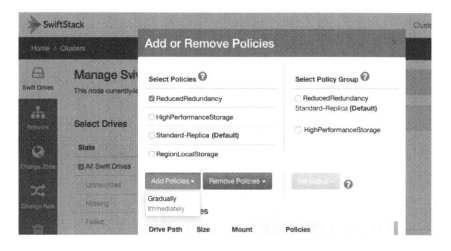

Adding capacity gradually with SwiftStack Controller Figure 4-5

In contrast if the "Add Gradually" button is used, the SwiftStack Controller will slowly add part of the new capacity and allow the data to safely redistribute itself before adding the next increment. The SwiftStack Controller will also track information about replication activity so it knows when to do the next increment. On the node monitoring page, you can see the percentage of completion for each device. Once complete, on the Manage Node page, the drive's status will go from "Adding" to "In Use".

Capacity Planning

Earlier we suggested keeping the cluster at least 10-20% free, SwiftStack makes this easier with its Capacity Planning tab. Since data is distributed fairly evenly across the cluster, how full the majority of the drives are will correspond to how full the overall cluster is. The Capacity Planning tab provides information about the capacity of the drives grouped by storage policies. Each policy has the amount of free space, used space, and percentages relating to how full the devices are.

The tab also provides two graphs:

Total and Used Cluster Capacity

When the "Total Bytes Used" value approaches the Recommended Max Fill line, it is time to add new drives.

Cluster Capacity

The Fill Rate metrics help predict at what rate additional capacity will need to be added. Where the "Least-Free Single-Drive Fill Rate" is a measure of how fast the cluster is filling and the "30-day Fill Rate" is the rate at which the least-free drive would be full in 30 days, assuming the present fill rate. Basically this means that if the Least-Free Single-Drive Fill Rate exceeds the 30-day Fill Rate, then this is an indication, all things being equal, that the cluster will be full within 30 days.

This capacity data helps users determine when to order additional capacity based on rates of storage growth. Being able to anticipate and address capacity shortages is an important part of managing data growth, especially in industries like life sciences where the data may have periodic, cyclic, or other identifiable growth patterns.

Rolling No Downtime Upgrades

A storage system should not need to become unavailable when capacity is added or when a system is being upgraded. Earlier we saw how

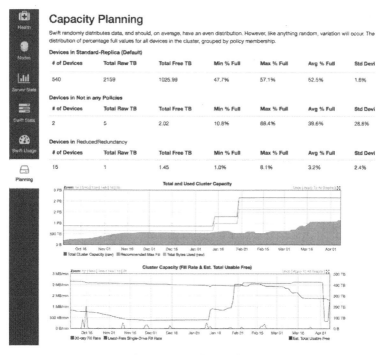

Capacity planning with SwiftStack Figure 4-6

capacity can be added incrementally without interruption to the object storage system. SwiftStack can also perform system upgrades without downtime.

This is especially important as sequence runs can often take days, leaving few windows for planned outages or downtime. With Swift and SwiftStack system-wide upgrades can be performed without clients experiencing any downtime.

Rolling Swift upgrades with SwiftStack Controller Figure 4-7

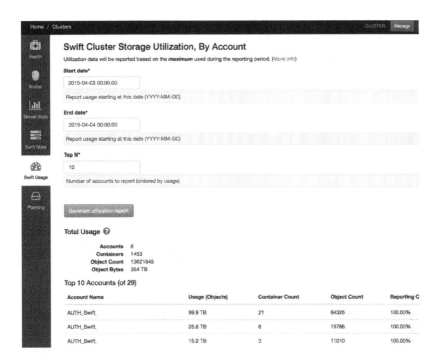

Utilization Reporting in the SwiftStack Controller Console Figure 4-8

During a typical Swift upgrade managed through SwiftStack, the following steps are performed on each node:

- Remove from the SwiftStack-managed load balancer
- 'Drain' current connections
- Shut down Swift
- Perform package upgrade
- Restart Swift
- Verify Swift health
- Return to load balancer

Utilization Reporting

The Swift Usage tab is a customizable report used for billing and usage queries that returns the total cluster usage and the top accounts by size over a given period of time This information is also available via API calls.

Undelete

Certain sequence data may be precious due to limited availability of

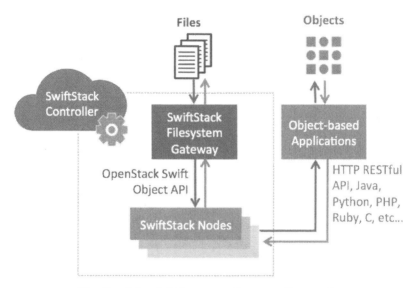

The SwiftStack Filesystem Gateway Figure 4-9

the sample, or particular sequence data may have to be retained for long periods of time due to regulatory concerns. SwiftStack provides a mechanism data retention beyond the user deletion date. For example, if a user deletes an object, it can be configured to be recoverable for a certain number of days.

Filesystem Gateway

SwiftStack's Filesystem Gateway provides a scalable file-based access to Swift. The SwiftStack Filesystem Gateway combines the advantages of object storage – scale, durability, availability, and low cost – with integration for existing file-based applications.

The Filesystem Gateway is an SMB/CIFS and NFS server. It exposes the configured filesystem(s), uses a cache to provide a temporary staging area for handling requests from clients, and uses the Swift API to read/write data on Swift storage. On the client side, users do not need to install third-party software. All they need to do is connect to the configured gateway and use shared folders to access their data.

Adding a SwiftStack Gateway to a SwiftStack Cluster is fairly simple and uses most of the same steps as installing a SwiftStack Node.

Conclusion

SwiftStack is the leading solution to deploy and manage OpenStack Swift. Beyond its core object storage capability, SwiftStack provides alerting, reporting, utilization data, its own interface and API as well as other capabilities needed by life sciences IT organizations.

In the next chapter we will dive more deeply into the internal architecture of OpenStack Swift.

Chapter Five

OpenStack Swift

So far in this book we have only hinted at how OpenStack Swift is designed and works. This chapter will fill in some details. We will look at the key characteristics of Swift, explain the fundamental concepts (accounts, containers, and objects), examine Swift's architecture, and discuss how Swift places data. We'll finish up by walking through a few scenarios to show how all these components work together. This chapter will also introduce you to the basics of the Swift API.

Swift Characteristics

Here is an overview of Swift's characteristics:

- Swift is an object storage system that is part of the OpenStack project.

- Swift is open-source and freely available.
- Swift can be used as a stand-alone storage system or as part of a cloud compute environment.
- Swift runs on standard Linux distributions and on standard x86 server hardware.
- Swift — like Amazon S3 — has an eventual consistency architecture, which make it ideal for building massive, highly distributed infrastructures with lots of unstructured data serving global sites.
- All objects (data) stored in Swift have a URL.
- Applications store and retrieve data in Swift via an indus try-standard RESTful HTTP API.
- Objects can have extensive metadata, which can be indexed and searched.
- All objects are stored with multiple copies and are replicated in as-unique-as-possible availability zones and/or regions.
- Swift is scaled by adding additional nodes, which allows for cost-effective linear storage expansion.
- When adding or replacing hardware, data does not have to be migrated to a new storage system (i.e. there is no need for forklift upgrades).
- Failed nodes and drives can be swapped out while the cluster is running with no downtime. New nodes and drives can be added the same way.

Up to now, we have just been saying that Swift can store objects. To be more precise, Swift enables users to store, retrieve, and delete objects (with their associated metadata) in containers via a RESTful HTTP API. Swift can also be accessed with HTTP requests directly to the API or by using one of the many Swift client libraries such as Java, Python, Ruby, or JavaScript. According to the industry analyst firm Gartner, Swift is the most widely used OpenStack project. Swift powers the largest object storage clouds, including Rackspace Cloud Files, the HP Cloud, IBM Softlayer Cloud, and countless private object storage clusters. This increasing adoption means that many of the most popular backup and content management applications now support Swift's HTTP API.

Nearly everyone reading this will be familiar with Hypertext Transfer

Protocol (HTTP) and particularly how it is used on the Web - a client sends a GET request to a web server and gets back the requested webpage or resource (e.g. PDF, mp3 or other files). However HTTP has a bigger vocabulary than just GET - including PUT, HEAD, POST, and DELETE, and Swift is fluent in all of them.

Swift Requests & Responses

Communication with a Swift cluster is done via HTTP using a RESTful API which results in every request having a response returned. This request and response pairing is a fundamental part of HTTP communication. All requests sent to Swift are made up of at least three parts:

- HTTP verb (e.g., GET, PUT, DELETE)
- Authentication information
- Storage URL
- Data or metadata to be written or read (optional depending on the request type)

The HTTP verb provides the action of the request. For example, "I want to PUT this object into the cluster" or "I want to GET this account information out of the cluster." The authentication information confirms the identity of the sender and verifies that the request is allowed to be fulfilled. The storage URL has two purposes -- it is the cluster address where the request should be sent and it's the storage location in the cluster where the requested action should take place.

A storage URL in Swift for an object looks like this:

https://swift.example.com/v1/account/container/object

Using the example above, we can break the storage URL into its two main parts:

- Cluster location: swift.example.com/v1/
- Storage location (for an object): /account/container/object

The storage location is given in one of three formats:
/account

> The account storage location is a uniquely named storage area that contains the metadata (descriptive information) about the account itself, as well as the list of containers in the account.

> It is important to keep in mind that in Swift, an account is not a user identity. When you hear account, think storage area.

/account/container

> The container storage location is the user-defined storage area within an account where metadata about the container itself and the list of objects in the container will be stored.

/account/container/object

> The object storage location is where the object itself and its metadata will be stored.

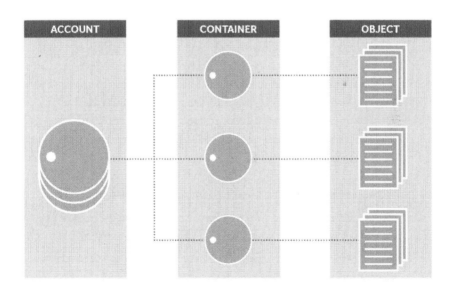

Account, containers, and objects Figure 5-1

The Swift HTTP API

A command–line client interface, such as curl, is all you need to perform simple operations on your Swift cluster. But many users require more sophisticated client applications. Behind the scenes, all Swift applications, including the command–line clients, use Swift's HTTP API to access the cluster.

Swift's HTTP API is RESTful, meaning that it exposes every container and object as a unique URL, and maps HTTP methods (like PUT, GET, POST, and DELETE) to the common data management operations (Create, Read, Update, and Destroy—collectively known as CRUD).

Swift makes use of most HTTP verbs including:

- GET — downloads objects, lists the contents of containers or accounts
- PUT — uploads objects, creates containers, overwrites metadata headers
- POST — creates containers if they don't exist, updates metadata (accounts or containers), overwrites metadata (objects)
- DELETE — deletes objects and containers that are empty
- HEAD — retrieves header information for the account, container, or object

Let's use curl, and an example storage URL *https://swift.example.com/v1/account*, to show how some sample HTTP GET requests could be used for objects, containers, or accounts. Common tasks a user might perform with GET include:

Downloading an object with a GET request to the object's storage URL:

```
curl -X GET https://swift.example.com/v1/account/
container/object
```

Listing objects in a container with a GET request to the container's storage URL:

```
curl -X GET https://swift.example.com/v1/account/
container/
```

Listing all containers in an account with a GET request to the account's storage URL:

```
curl -X GET https://swift.example.com/v1/account/
```

While a CLI like curl is all that is needed to perform simple operations on a Swift cluster, many people will want to use Swift client libraries to have applications make those underlying HTTP requests.

Client Libraries

Application developers can construct HTTP requests and parse HTTP responses using their programming language's HTTP client or they may choose to use open-source language bindings to abstract away the details of the HTTP interface. Open–source client libraries are available for most modern programming languages, including:

- Python
- Ruby
- PHP
- C#/.NET
- Java
- JavaScript

What happens once a request is sent to the cluster? Before we take a look at how the cluster handles a request, first let's look at how a cluster is put together.

Swift Overview — Processes

A Swift cluster is the distributed storage system used for object storage.

It is a collection of machines that are running Swift's server processes and consistency services. Each machine running one or more Swift processes and services is called a node.

The four Swift server processes are proxy, account, container, and object. When a node has only the proxy server process running it is called a proxy node. Nodes running one or more of the other server processes (account, container, or object) will often be called a storage node. Storage nodes contain the data that incoming requests wish to affect, e.g. a PUT request for an object would go to the appropriate nodes running the object server processes. Storage nodes will also have a number of other services running on them to maintain data consistency.

When talking about the same server processes running on the nodes in a cluster we call it the server process layers. e.g., proxy layer, account layer, container layer, and object layer. Let's look a little more closely at the server process layers.'

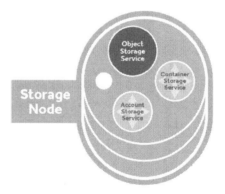

Server processes running on a node Figure 5-2

Server Process Layers
Proxy Layer

The proxy server processes are the public face of Swift as they are the only ones that communicate with external clients. As a result they are the first and last to handle an API request. All requests to and responses from the proxy use standard HTTP verbs and response codes.

Proxy servers use a shared-nothing architecture and can be scaled as needed based on projected workloads. A minimum of two proxy servers should be deployed for redundancy. Should one proxy server fail, the others will take over.

For example, if a valid request is sent to Swift then the proxy server will verify the request, determine the correct storage nodes responsible for the data (based on a hash of the object name), and send the request to those servers concurrently. If the primary storage nodes are unavailable, the proxy will choose appropriate hand-off nodes to send the request to. The nodes will return a response and the proxy will, in turn, return the first response (and data if it was requested) to the requester.

Remember that the proxy server process is looking up multiple locations because Swift provides data durability by writing multiple — typically three — complete copies of the data and storing them in the system.

Account Layer

The account server process handles requests regarding metadata for the individual accounts or the list of the containers within each account. This information is stored by the account server process in SQLite databases on disk.

Container Layer

The container server process handles requests regarding container metadata or the list of objects within each container. It's important to note that the list of objects doesn't contain information about the location of the object, simply that it belongs to a specific container. Like accounts, the container information is stored as SQLite databases.

Object Layer

The object server process is responsible for the actual storage of objects on the drives of its node. Objects are stored as binary files on the drive using a path that is made up in part of its associated partition (which we will discuss shortly) and the operation's timestamp. The object's metadata (standard and custom) is stored in the file's extended attributes (xattrs) which means that the data and metadata are stored together and copied as a single unit.

Consistency Services

A key aspect of Swift is that it was built with the knowledge that failures happen and was built to work around them. When account, container, or object server processes are running on a node, it means that data is being stored there. This means that consistency services will also be running on those nodes to ensure the integrity and availability of the data.

The two main consistency services are auditors and replicators. There are also a number of specialized services that run in support of individual server processes, e.g., the account reaper that runs where account server processes are running.

Auditors

Auditors run in the background on every storage node in a Swift cluster and continually scan the disks to ensure that the data stored on disk has not suffered any bit-rot or file system corruption. There are account auditors, container auditors, and object auditors which run to support their corresponding server process.

If an error is found, the auditor moves the corrupted object to a quarantine area.

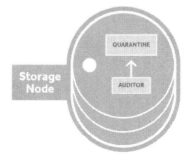

Auditors examine data and move it to a quarantine area if any errors are found Figure 5-3

Replicators

Account, container, and object replicator processes run in the background on all nodes that are running the corresponding services. A replicator will continuously examine its local node and compare the accounts, containers, and objects against the copies on other nodes in the cluster. If one of the other nodes has an old or missing copy, then the replicator will send a copy of its local data out to that node. Replicators only push their local data out to other nodes; they do not

pull in remote copies if their local data is missing or out of date.

The replicator also handles object and container deletions. Object deletion starts by creating a zero-byte tombstone file that is the latest version of the object. This version is then replicated to the other nodes and the object is removed from the entire system.

Container deletion can only happen with an empty container. It will be marked as deleted and the replicators will push this version out.

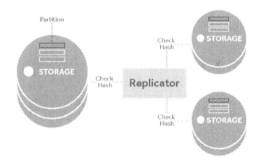

Replicators examine the checksums of partitions Figure 5-4

Specialized Consistency Services

Container and Object Updaters

The container updater service runs to support accounts. It will update:

- container listings in the accounts
- account metadata (object count, container count, bytes used)

The object updater runs to support containers, but as a redundant service. The object server process is the primary updater. Only if it fails with an update attempt will the object updater take over and then update:

- object listing in the containers
- container metadata (object count, bytes used)

Object Expirer

The object expirer service purges data that is designated as expired.

Account Reaper

When an account reaper service makes its rounds on a node and finds an account marked as deleted, it starts stripping out all objects and containers associated with the account. With each pass it will continue to dismantle the account until it is emptied and removed. The reaper has a delay value that can be configured so the reaper will wait before it starts deleting data. This is used to guard against erroneous deletions.

Swift Overview—Cluster Architecture

Nodes

A node is a machine that is running one or more Swift processes. When there are multiple nodes running that provide all the processes needed for Swift to act as a distributed storage system they are considered a cluster.

Within a cluster the nodes will also belong to two logical groups: regions and nodes. Regions and nodes are user-defined and identify unique characteristics about a collection of nodes - usually geographical location and points of failure, such as all the power running to one rack of nodes. These ensure that Swift can place data across different parts of the cluster to reduce risk.

Regions

Regions are user-defined and usually indicate when parts of the cluster are physically separate - usually a geographical boundary. A cluster has a minimum of one region and there are many single region clusters as a result. A cluster that is using two or more regions is a multi-region cluster.

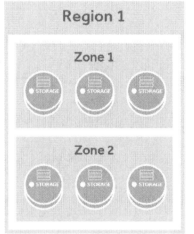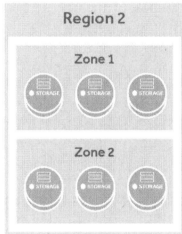

Storage zones can be deployed across geographic regions Figure 5-5

When a read request is made, the proxy layer favors nearby copies of the data as measured by latency. When a write request is made the proxy layer, by default, writes to all the locations simultaneously. There is an option called write affinity that, when enabled, allows the cluster to write all copies locally and then transfer them asynchronously to the other regions

Zones

Within regions, Swift allows availability zones to be configured to isolate failure boundaries. An availability zone should be defined by a distinct set of physical hardware whose failure would be isolated from other zones. In a large deployment, availability zones may be defined as unique facilities in a large data center campus. In a single datacenter deployment, the availability zones may be different racks. While there does need to be at least one zone in a cluster, it is far more common for a cluster to have many zones.

Storage can be placed in distinct fault-tolerant zones Figure 5-6

Swift Overview—Data Placement

We have previously mentioned that there are several locations for data because Swift makes copies and stores them across the cluster. This section cover this process in greater detail.

When the server processes or the consistency services need to locate data they will look at the storage location (/account, /account/container, /account/container/object) and consult one of the three rings: account ring, container ring, or object ring.

Each Swift ring is a modified consistent hashing ring that is distributed to every node in the cluster. The boiled down version is that a modified consistent hashing ring contains a pair of lookup tables that the Swift processes and services use to determine data locations. One table has the information about the drives in the cluster and the other has the table used to look up where any piece of account, container, or object data should be placed. That second table — where to place things — is the more complicated one to populate. Before we further discuss the rings and how they are built we should cover partitions and replicas as they are critical concepts to understanding the rings.

Partitions

Swift wants to store data uniformly across the cluster and have it be available quickly for requests. The developers of Swift tried various methods and designs before settling on the current variation of the modified consistent hashing ring.

Hashing is the key to the data locations. When a process, like a proxy server process, needs to find where data is stored for a request, it will call on the appropriate ring to get a value that it needs to correctly hash the storage location (the second part of the storage URL). The hash value of the storage location will map to a partition value.

This hash value will be one of hundreds or thousands of hash values that could be calculated when hashing storage locations. The full range of possible hash values is the "hashing ring" part of a modified consistent hashing ring.

The "consistent" part of a modified consistent hashing ring is where partitions come into play. The full range of hash values in a hashing ring is chopped up into numerous smaller ranges. Each of these parts of the hashing ring, called partitions, can be mapped to a drive. As drives are added or removed storage, they would be mapped randomly around the ring and either take hash ranges from or release hash ranges to the mapped drives that were adjacent to it. Over time this would produce partitions with much larger and much smaller ranges than the average which increases the likelihood that objects will be unavailable during capacity changes.

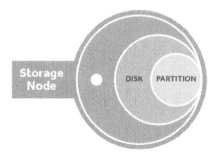

The relationship of a storage node, a disk, and a partition Figure 5-7

To address the churn and availability issues, Swift uses a modified consistent hashing ring where the partitions are a set number and uniform in size. As a ring is built the partitions are assigned to drives in the cluster. This implementation is conceptually simple — a partition is just a directory sitting on a disk with a corresponding hash table of what it contains.

Storage nodes have disks. Partitions are represented as directories on each disk.

While the size and number of partitions does not change, the number of drives in the cluster does. The more drives in a cluster the fewer partitions per drive. For a simple example, if there were 150 partitions and 2 drives then each drive would have 75 partitions mapped to it. If a new drive is added then each of the 3 drives would have 50 partitions.

Partitions are the smallest unit that Swift likes to work with — data is added to partitions, consistency processes will check partitions, and partitions are moved to new drives. By having many of the actions happen at the partition level Swift is able to keep processor and network traffic low. This also means that as the system scales up, behavior continues to be predictable as the number of partitions remains fixed.

Replicas

Swift's durability and resilience to failure depends in large part on its replicas. The more replicas used, the more protection against losing data when there is a failure. This is especially true in clusters that have separate data centers and geographic regions to spread the replicas across.

When we say replicas, we mean partitions that are replicated. Most commonly a replica count of three is chosen. During the initial creation of the Swift rings, every partition is replicated and each replica is placed as uniquely as possible across the cluster. Each subsequent rebuilding of the rings will calculate which, if any, of the replicated partitions need to be moved to a different drive. Part of partition replication includes designating handoff drives. When a drive fails, the replication/auditing processes notice and push the missing data to handoff locations. The probability that all replicated partitions across the system will become corrupt (or otherwise fail) before the cluster notices and is able to push the data to handoff locations is very small, which is why we say that Swift is durable.

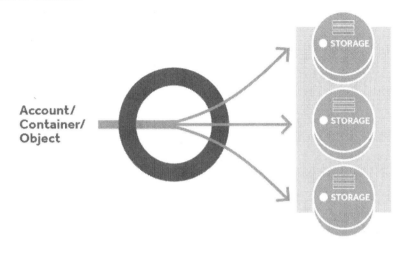

An object ring enables an /account/container/object path to be mapped to partitions Figure 5-8

Previously we talked about proxy server processes using a hash of the data's storage location to determine where in the cluster that data is located. We can now be more precise and say that the proxy server process is locating the three replicated partitions each of which contains a copy of the data.

Erasure Codes

Erasure codes are like fractional replicas. The basic idea is to break up the original data into smaller pieces and compute a set of chunks of data so that you can recreate any missing pieces if you lose them, up to a certain number of chunks. With a Reed-Solomon encoding, data is broken into m data chunks and then k parity chunks are computed (for a total of n chunks). So a 10+4 scheme has 14 total chunks and can withstand the loss of any 4 chunks.

In Swift, the ring stores a primary partition for each of the total number of chunks, e.g. 14 in a 10+4 scheme. As data comes into the cluster, it is encoded and the chunks are spread out throughout the cluster. This gives you very good durability without all the overhead of full replicas. In a 10+4 scheme, there is a 40% overhead in storage: 40 additional MB are stored for every 100 MB of content. In a triple-replicated scheme, there is a 200% overhead: 200 additional MB are stored for every 100MB of content.

Erasure codes are not without cost, however. Erasure codes require a lot of computation on the data every time it is read and written. Also, since the data is stored in more places, every request to read or write the data must connect to more servers in the cluster. The additional network connection overhead and the additional CPU requirement mean that erasure coded storage schemes are great for large objects that are less-frequently accessed.

The Rings

With partitions and replicas defined, we can now look at the data structure of the rings. Each of the Swift rings is a modified consistent hashing ring. This ring data structure includes the partition shift value, which processes and services use to determine the hash of a storage location. It also has two important internal data structures: the devices list and the devices lookup table.

The devices list is populated with all the devices that have been added to a special ring building file. Each entry for a drive includes its ID number, zone, weight, IP, port, and device name.

The devices lookup table has one row per replica and one column per partition in the cluster. This generates a table that is typically three rows by thousands of columns. During the building of a ring, Swift calculates the best drive to place each partition replica on using the drive weights and the unique-as-possible placement algorithm. It then records that drive in the table.

Recall the proxy server process that was looking up data. The proxy server process calculated the hash value of the storage location which maps to a partition value. The proxy server process then uses this partition value on the devices lookup table. The process will check the first replica row in the partition column to determine the device ID where the first replica is located. The process will search the next two rows to get the other two locations. In our figure the partition value was 2 and the process found that the data was located on drives 1, 8, and 10.

		Partitions				
		0	1	2	3	4	...
Replicas	0	7	0	1	4	22
	1	12	4	8	10	18
	2	1	21	10	0	3

Ring component: Devices lookup table Figure 5-9

For erasure codes, each partition is mapped to the total chunks for the erasure code scheme. For example, in a 10+4 scheme, the ring would have a partition mapped to 14 different devices.

The proxy server process can then make a second set of searches on the devices list to get the information about all three drives, including ID numbers, zones, weights, IPs, ports, and device names. With this information the process can call on the correct drives. In our example figure, the process determined the ID number, zone, weight, IP, port, and device name for device 1.

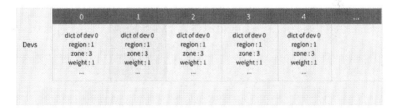

	0	1	2	3	4	...
Devs	dict of dev 0	dict of dev 0	dict of dev 0	dict of dev 0	dict of dev 0	
	region : 1	region : 1	region : 1	region : 1	region : 1	
	zone : 3	zone : 3	zone : 3	zone : 3	zone : 3	
	weight : 1	weight : 1	weight : 1	weight : 1	weight : 1	
	...	...	...	...	...	

Ring component: Devices list Figure 5-10

Let's take a closer look at how partitions are calculated and how they are mapped to drives.

Building a Ring

When a ring is being built the total number of partitions is calculated with a value called the partition power. Once set, during the initial creation of a cluster, the partition power should not be changed. This means that the total number of partitions will remain the same in the cluster. The formula used is 2 raised to the partition power. For example if a partition power of 13 is picked, then the total partitions in a cluster is 2^{13} or 8192.

During the very first building of the rings, all partitions will need to be assigned to the available drives. When the rings are rebuilt, called rebalancing, only partitions that need to be moved to different drives, usually because drives were added or removed, will be affected.

The placement of the partitions is determined by a combination of replica count, replica lock, and data distribution mechanisms such as drive weight and unique-as-possible placement.

Replica Count

Remember that it is not just partitions but also the replicated copies that must be placed on the drives. For a cluster with a partition power of 13 and a replica count of 3, there will be a total of 8192 partitions and 24576 (which is 3*8192) total replicated partitions that will be placed on the drives. For erasure codes, the "replica count" is the total number of nodes for the algorithm used (e.g. 14 in a 10+4 scheme).

Replica Lock

While a partition is being moved, Swift will lock that partition's replicas so that they are not eligible to be moved for a period of time to ensure data availability. This is used both when the rings are being updated as well as operationally when data is moved. It is not used with the very first building of the rings. The exact length of time to lock a partition is set by the min_part_hours configuration option which is often set to a default of 24 hours.

Weight

Swift uses a value called weight for each drive in the cluster. This user-defined value, set when the drive is added, is the drive's relative weight compared to the other drives in the ring. The weight helps the cluster calculate how many partitions should be assigned to the drive. The higher the weight, the greater number of partitions Swift should assign to the drive.

Unique-as-possible Placement

To ensure that the cluster is storing data evenly across its defined spaces (regions, zones, nodes, and disks), Swift assigns partitions using a unique-as-possible placement algorithm. This algorithm identifies the least-used place in the cluster to place a partition. First it looks for the least used region; if all the regions contain a partition it then looks for the least used zone, then server (IP:port), and finally the least-used disk, and places the partition there. The least-used formula also attempts to place the partitions as far from each other as possible.

If a cluster cannot be balanced (e.g. if it has differently sized zones), then Swift attempts to balance it such that every drive is evenly filled until the smallest zone is full. Then any remaining partitions to be placed are put into the larger zones, overweighting them but enabling cluster capacity to be effectively utilized. This allows for clusters to easily expand with new zones and regions without immediately causing a huge amount of data movement in the cluster.

Once Swift calculates and records the placement of all the partitions, then the ring can be created. One account ring will be generated for a cluster and be used to determine where the account data is located. One container ring will be generated for a cluster and be used to determine where the container data is located. One object ring will be generated for a cluster and be used to determine where the object data is located.

There is a great deal to say about how Swift works internally and we encourage those who are interested in learning more to read the OpenStack Swift documentation.

Swift HTTP Requests: A Closer Look

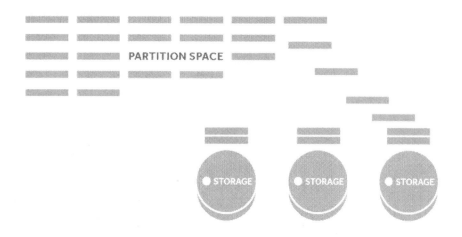

The partition space is distributed across all available storage Figure 5-11

Now that we have covered the basics of Swift, we can look at how this all works together. Let's see how a cluster handles an incoming request.

As mentioned earlier, all requests sent to Swift are made up of at least three parts:

- HTTP verb (e.g., GET, PUT, DELETE)
- Authentication information
- Storage URL (swift.example.com/v1/account)
  - Cluster location: swift.example.com/v1/
  - Storage location (for an object): /account/container/object
- Optional data or metadata (depending on the request)

The request is sent to the cluster location which is a hook into the proxy layer. The proxy layer first handles the request verifying auth. Once the request passes auth the proxy layer will route the incoming request to the appropriate storage nodes.

For our examples below, we will assume that the client has valid credentials and permission for the actions being taken and that the cluster uses three replicas.

Example: PUT

A client uses the Swift API to make an HTTP request to PUT an

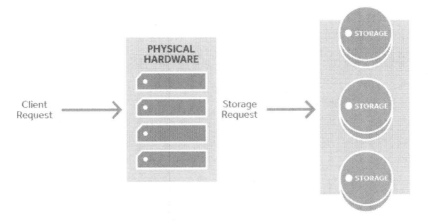

Client request arrives to the cluster (physical hardware) and is routed as a storage request to the correct storage nodes Figure 5-12

object into an existing container. Swift receives the request and one of the proxy server processes will handle it. First the proxy server process will verify auth and then it will take the hash of the storage location and look up all three partition locations (the drives) where the data should be stored using the object ring. The process then uses the object ring to look up the IP and other information for those three devices.

Having determined the location of all three partitions, the proxy server process sends the object to each storage node where it is placed in the appropriate partition. When a quorum is reached, in this case when at least two of the three writes are returned as successful, then the proxy server process will notify the client that the upload was successful.

Next, the container database is updated asynchronously to reflect the new object in it.

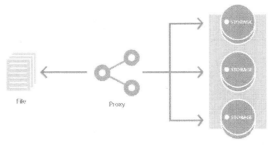

Quorum writes ensure durability Figure 5-13

Example: GET

A client uses the Swift API to make an HTTP request to GET an object from the cluster. Swift receives the request and one of the proxy server processes will handle it. First the proxy server process will verify auth and then it will take the hash of the storage location and look up all three partition locations (the drives) where the data should be stored using the object ring. The process then uses the object ring to look up the IP and other information for those three devices.

Having determined the location of all three partitions, the proxy server process will request the object from each storage node and return the object to the client.

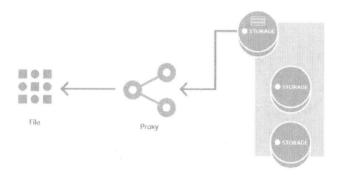

Get requests are handled by one of the storage nodes Figure 5-14

Additional Swift Capabilities

Since Swift is written in Python, it is very flexible and can be extended with middleware that plug into the WSGI pipeline. By adding middleware in Swift's proxy layer, it can be extended with additional features not possible in other storage systems. Some of these features and integrations include:

Active checksum checking

Swift stores an MD5 checksum with each object. The checksum is not only checked by internal auditing processes, but is also returned in the header with each request. If the checksum doesn't match, both the storage system and the client can toss away the result and fetch one of the other protected replicas.

Static website hosting

You can host and serve files such as BAM/VCF files directly from the storage system. Rather than building a custom application, these files can be directly served from the cluster using HTTP. Static websites can be built to host and serve the data.

Automatically expiring objects

During some stages of a genomics workflow, data only needs to be stored temporarily. Objects can be given an expiry time after which they are no longer available and will be deleted.

Time-limited URLs

Some applications create data that needs to be temporarily public. URLs can be generated that are valid for only a limited period of time. These URLs can be used to build a "drop box" for large files that enable temporary write permissions without needing to hand out full credentials to an unauthenticated party.

Direct-from-HTML-form uploads

Working with time-limited URLs, web forms can be built that upload data directly into Swift so that it doesn't have to be proxied through another server.

Quotas

Storage limits can be set on containers and accounts.

Versioned writes

When a new version of an object is uploaded, a container can be configured so that older versions of the object will be retained

Support for chunked Transfer-Encoding

Users can upload data to Swift without knowing ahead of time how large the object is.

Multi-Range reads

Users can read one or more sections of an object with only one read request.

Access control lists

Users can configure access to their data to enable or prevent others' ability to read or write the data.

Programmatic access to data locality

Deployers can integrate Swift with HPC systems and take advantage of locality information to lower network requirements when processing data.

Conclusion

In this chapter you've become acquainted with the key concepts that Swift uses to organize, distribute, and serve data using:

- Accounts and containers to create unique namespaces for objects
- Proxy servers to route requests for reads and writes
- Storage services for accounts, containers, and objects to store the data
- The partition space to store all the replicas for accounts, containers, and objects
- The ring to map partitions to physical locations
- and replicators, auditors, and updaters to keep everything consistent

In the next chapters, we will provide some practical advice on how to get started, architect, and use SwiftStack.

## Chapter Six

Getting Started with SwiftStack

This chapter looks at how to install SwiftStack, which automates the installation and management of OpenStack Swift clusters. SwiftStack includes an unmodified version of OpenStack Swift, along with proprietary software components for deployment, integration (with authentication, billing, and external monitoring systems), and management of one or more Swift clusters. Further details can be found at the SwiftStack's website (swiftstack.com).

To get started with SwiftStack, first signup for a SwiftStack account at: http://swiftstack.com/signup/.

Before we move on to installation, we should briefly describe the two main components: the SwiftStack Controller and the SwiftStack Node.

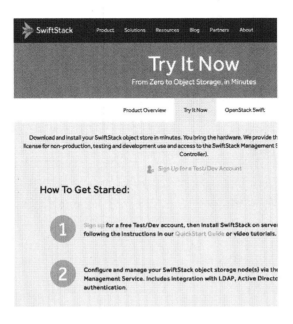

swiftstack.com – where to get started with SwiftStaFigure 6-1

SwiftStack Controller

The SwiftStack Controller provides the management plane for one or more clusters. As an out-of-band management system, the SwiftStack Controller decouples control from the actual storage nodes and instead can manage storage nodes remotely over the Internet or be deployed on-premises next to the storage cluster. For an operator, the Controller provides a browser-based interface for easier control and management of clusters.

Users sign in to the Controller's web interface and go to their cluster page. From there they can change cluster settings, add or remove capacity, and address notifications of component failures.

It starts with the creation of an account, called the organization, on the Controller. Once an organization is created on the Controller, users can be added. SwiftStack Controller users, depending on their permissions, can:

- Create more SwiftStack Controller user accounts for their

organization

- Create and configure their cluster(s)
- Quickly and easily add or remove nodes and drives from their cluster(s)
- Create users for their cluster(s) using the SwiftStack auth system
- Configure an external auth (LDAP, Keystone) for their cluster(s)
- Tune and enable or disable middleware for their cluster(s)
- View the monitoring and health data for their cluster(s)
- Perform rolling upgrades of the Swift version on their nodes with no downtime

To understand how the SwiftStack Controller works, let's review some of the key features.

Deployment Automation

SwiftStack Nodes, which we discuss in greater detail later on, have agents which identify the available devices. The SwiftStack Controller receives this inventory and displays it to the cluster operator, who can then configure and manage these devices on each node. The devices themselves get unique SwiftStack identifiers so that an inventory can be kept and devices can be consistently remounted in the event that they get reshuffled in the same system, or are placed in an entirely new chassis.

Once the Controller has established a connection with a specific SwiftStack Node, the cluster operator can initiate several different setup and deployment tasks via the Controller's interface, including:

- Configuring network interfaces
- Configuring nodes and formatting drives
- Deploying account, container, and object rings
- Configuring availability zones and regions based on hardware topology

On large clusters, operators might prefer to automate this process by writing scripts based on command-line commands or integrating it with configuration management tools, such as Chef or Puppet.

Ring Management

The SwiftStack Controller keeps track of all the devices and provides an interface for cluster operators to add or remove capacity. When these capacity changes require the generation of new rings, the SwiftStack Controller will create the rings and copy them to each node in the cluster. This means that when it's time to add more storage capacity, it can be done safely without interruptions. Likewise, data can be slowly migrated off a failing drive or a decommissioned node.

Node and Cluster Monitoring

The SwiftStack Controller provides the metrics you need to make informed decisions to properly manage and scale your cluster. It provides alerts on drive failures, node failures, and any other issues it detects.

The SwiftStack Controller also collects hundreds of data points on each node and aggregates data from multiple systems into a single cluster-wide view that allows you to zoom in on events across a specific timeframe. The controller will generate reports, including a report for capacity planning and a report on storage use for chargeback and billing.

SwiftStack monitoring can also be integrated with Ganglia, Nagios, and other monitoring tools.

SwiftStack Node

SwiftStack Nodes are servers with the SwiftStack Node software installed. At this writing, there are installers for CentOS/RedHat Server and Ubuntu Server. During installation the latest vanilla release of Swift as well as SwiftStack processes and agents are set up and started.

While Swift is the object storage engine on a SwiftStack Node, it is the SwiftStack agents and processes that are establish secure communications with the SwiftStack Controller, monitor the Node's health, report alerts and utilization metrics as well as participate in integrations like LDAP authentication.

Creating a SwiftStack Node to add to your cluster on your SwiftStack Controller account is a simple process that results in the installation of the:

- Latest stable version of OpenStack Swift
- Dependencies needed for Swift
- SwiftStack management agents for monitoring Node health and communication with the Controller
- SwiftStack integrations for Swift, including authentication modules for systems such as LDAP
- SSL termination
- SwiftStack load balancer

Once installed, configuration of SwiftStack Node software takes place on the SwiftStack Controller web interface. There, a cluster operator can enter the networking details and designate the Node to have proxy services, storage (account, container, object) services, or both running on it.

Once the Node is added to the cluster from the Controller, its services are started and it becomes a fully functional member of the cluster. It behaves the same as a typical Swift node but also has those SwiftStack processes that run in the background for SwiftStack management and communication.

Among these processes are the SwiftStack agents that establish a VPN connection with the Controller. With this connection, a cluster operator can manage SwiftStack Node via the Controller. The Node accepts only a limited number of commands from the Controller, specifically:

- Pushing new configuration files
- Activating new configurations
- Querying devices for drive discovery/inventory synchronization
- Formatting devices

- Unmounting devices
- Querying for network interfaces
- Querying for general system information (RAM/hostname/ CPU core count)

At no point does the Controller have access to the data stored on a SwiftStack Node.

Creating a Swift Cluster Using SwiftStack

For the following example we use a SwiftStack Controller provided as a service over the Internet rather than an on-premises Controller. Email contact@swiftstack.com for more information about installing an on-premises SwiftStack Controller.

For those already running an on-premises SwiftStack Controller, wherever you see https://platform.swiftstack.com in the following example, replace it with the hostname for your private controller, e.g., *https://swiftstack-controller.private.example.com.*

Creating a SwiftStack Controller User

As mentioned earlier, once a company has established an organization account on a Controller, SwiftStack Controller users can be added.

A cluster operator, using a SwiftStack Controller user account with the correct permissions set, can add nodes to the Controller. Creating a user is a simple task that the person or team in your organization with a SwiftStack Controller administrator account can perform.

Once you have a SwiftStack Controller user account in your organization, you are ready to proceed.

Installing the SwiftStack Node Software

The machine on which you will be installing the SwiftStack Node software needs:

1. A plain installation of CentOS/Red Hat Server 6.3, 6.4, 6.5, 7.0 (64-bit), or Ubuntu 12.04 LTS Precise Server, 14.04 LTS Trusty (64-bit).
2. Access to its SwiftStack Controller for the initial download of the SwiftStack Node software. This initial claim process and configuration requires communication over HTTPS (port 443).

Note: all installation commands need to be performed as root.

On the server, run:

```
curl   https://platform.swiftstack.com/install   |
bash
```

Once the software is installed, the new SwiftStack Node contacts the Controller via HTTPS (port 443). If successful, the Node receives a unique identifier from the Controller. It then constructs a claim URL and displays it in the terminal. This confirms that the installation process is complete.

```
+------------------------------------------------+
| Your claim URL is:                             |
|https://platform.swiftstack.com/claim/3e8730    |
|21-8da3-11e2-9108-000c29f59d79                  |
+------------------------------------------------+
```

When installation is complete, the SwiftStack Node will open a secure VPN connection to the Controller over UDP (port 1194). This only allows outgoing connections from the Node over the VPN connection—no connections are allowed to the Node from the Controller.

Claiming a New Node

Once the claim URL is displayed, you should open a web browser and sign into the Controller with your SwiftStack Controller user account.

Once signed in, you can copy and paste the claim URL in the browser.

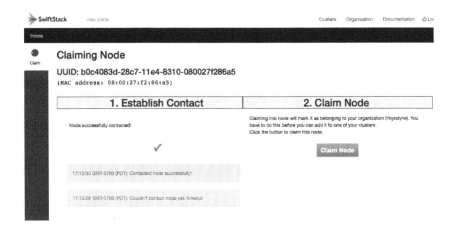

Claiming a Node with the SwiftStack Controller Figure 6-2

The Node and Controller will attempt contact. When the Node is seen by the Controller, it will display a Claim Node button that you should click.

The Node and Controller will be using the secure VPN connection initiated by the Node to communicate. The Node's VPN connection will need to be able to communicate out over port 1194, the VPN (UDP) communications channel.

Creating a Cluster

After you click the Claim Node button, the Controller will prompt you to create a new cluster. If there is a preexisting cluster, you will also have the option to select that cluster. To create a cluster, provide the cluster's name and outward-facing IP address. You can also specify its hostname, SSL, NTP, and other advanced Swift options, if you wish.

Ingesting a Node

With the cluster created, the page will open to the Manage Nodes tab. You can select the region and zone for the new Node and then click on the Ingest Now button

Configuring a storage cluster with SwiftStack Figure 6-3

Configuring Network

Verify that your node's network interfaces have been discovered, and assign them correctly to Outward-facing interface and Cluster-facing interface. Click Reassign Interfaces.

Ingesting a new Node into a SwiftStack cluster Figure 6-4

Provisioning a SwiftStack Node

Once the Node is enabled, click on the Drives tab. You can start provisioning the Node by clicking on the Format button. All available drives will be marked for formatting; you can then click the Change button to begin formatting the drives (devices). Formatting drives may take a few minutes to complete

Once the drives are formatted, they will need to be added to various policies depending on their intended use. By default there is an account and container policy and a default object storage policy. If custom object storage policies had been created they will also be an available.

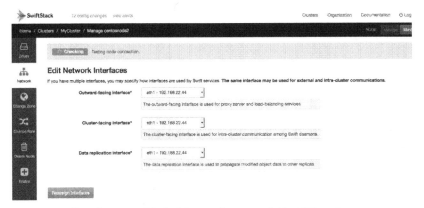

Configuring Node Networking with SwiftStack
Figure 6-5

Select the drives that need to be added to a policy and then click the "Add or Remove Policies" button. It can be noted that any drive can be assigned to store account/container data, but SwiftStack generally recommends using faster media such as SSDs to ensure that account and container listings are quick.

Mounting and formatting devices Figure 6-6

On the "Add or Remove Policies" popover window, you should see two policies to choose from: Account & Container and Standard-Replica. The former will put the selected drives into the Account & Container policies, which will allow them to respond to requests about Accounts and Containers. The latter, Standard-Replica, is the default Object policy that was created for your cluster. Check both boxes, click Add Policies, and then select Immediately from the dropdown.

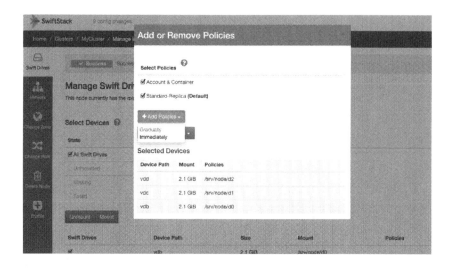

Mounting and formatting devices Figure 6-7

Adding Swift Users

The next step is to add a user for the cluster. We will add a user through the Controller using the SwiftStack auth system. Go to the Create a New User page and provide the desired username, password, and permission level for the user account.

The authentication system built into SwiftStack is a fast, flat file that is deployed on each Node with hashed passwords. Although it does require a configuration push out to the cluster, it does not require a proxy restart. Users can also be added programmatically through a REST API function.

Deploying to Cluster

With all the configurations set for your new cluster, it is time to apply them to the cluster. The Controller will display the Deploy SwiftStack Cluster page.

Once you click the Deploy Config to Cluster button, the cluster:

- Adds appropriate devices and nodes into the Swift builder files
- Creates the Swift rings
- Adds any additional user accounts that have been created or modified
- Creates new Swift configurations based on the changes made to the network and tuning tabs
- Provides the new configuration files, and restarts processes when necessary, for each node in the cluster

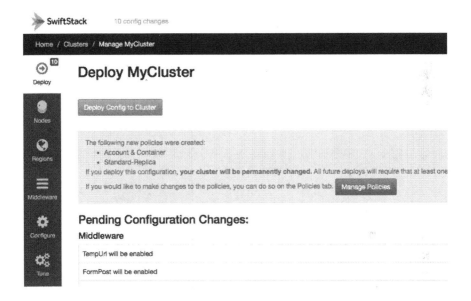

Deploying SwiftStack Cluster Figure 6-8

While the cluster is applying all these configurations, a "Pending Jobs" status message is displayed. When the configuration deployment is done, a "Job Finished" status message is displayed and your SwiftStack cluster will be accessible at the IP address you specified.

Creating a Container and Uploading an Object via Web Console

Although you can use many other tools using the Swift API, let's use the web console to show some of the additional capabilities of SwiftStack.

Installed on the SwiftStack Node will be a built-in web console for storage users to upload, download, and manage data. After the configuration deployment is completed, the Controller will display a link to the web console

Link to Web Console URL on the SwiftStack Controller Figure 6-9

Once you sign in to the account to which you want to upload an object, you can easily create a container and upload data

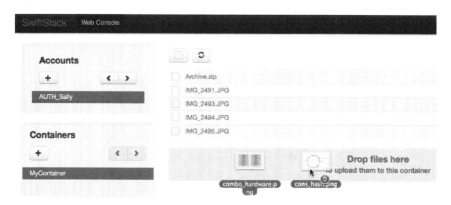

Uploading files with the SwiftStack Web Client Figure 6-10

Now you can upload files by dragging and dropping them, or using the upload button.

Conclusion

You have now seen how to install a cluster using SwiftStack. At this point you are hopefully understanding how the pieces of Swift fit together and seeing some of its power. Next we turn to applications for accessing your Swift cluster.

Chapter Seven

Applications: How to Access Object Storage

In addition to the SwiftStack Web Client there are many other methods for accessing a SwiftStack cluster. In this chapter we will cover some of the applications available in the context of life sciences. For more applications visit *https://swiftstack.com/partners/*

Command-line tool: Swift CLI

The Swift command-line is a great way to use a Swift cluster. The Swift CLI is part of the python-swiftclient package and can be installed on any computer running Python 2.6 or 2.7. Detailed installation instructions can be found at:

https://swiftstack.com/docs/integration/python-swiftclient.html

The swift command simplifies things for users, by saving some typing and making several common types of requests easier. However, this simplification comes at a cost: the Swift CLI (the command-line tool) is not able to do everything that Swift (the storage system) can. There are some types of HTTP requests that the Swift CLI does not yet know how to send.

One reason the swift command is popular is because it provides users with human-friendly verbs (upload instead of PUT) to use when communicating with a cluster. It then translates the commands into the appropriate HTTP verbs.

Configuration

Before you can access a Swift cluster with the command–line client, you need to authenticate, using three pieces of information:

1. your Swift cluster's auth URL
2. your username
3. your password (or API key)

You can find the auth URL for your Swift cluster on the Cluster page of the SwiftStack Controller console:

Cluster page of the SwiftStack Controller console Figure 7-1

With an auth URL and user credentials, you can construct a swift command–line, like so:

```
$ swift -A <auth URL> -U <username> -K <password>
<command>
```

We'll explain what to use for <command> in a moment, but for now the salient point is that you must pass your authentication credentials to the swift client. Since it would be cumbersome to provide these same parameters every time you execute a swift command, you can take advantage of some helpful environment variables to define your credentials just once per terminal session. In Linux and OS X, this looks like:

```
$ export ST_AUTH=<auth URL>
$ export ST_USER=<username>
$ export ST_KEY=<password>
```

Usage

Once you've set these environment variables, you no longer need to pass the credentials on the command line, simplifying your commands to:

```
$ swift <command>
```

For convenience, these environment variables can be set in a shell resource file, like .bashrc or .zshrc. Bear in mind that storing your Swift API key in a file like this might not be acceptable in more security-conscious environments.

Now that you know how to authenticate, you're ready to run swift commands against your cluster. The first thing you might like to do is see some basic information about the cluster, such as how many containers and objects you have in the cluster and how many bytes you're using. You can do this with the stat command:

```
$ swift stat
   Account: AUTH_account
Containers: 2
   Objects: 2
     Bytes: 2048
```

You can get a listing of all the containers in the account with the list command:

```
$ swift list
animals
vegetables
```

Here you see that you have two containers. You can create new containers with the post command:

```
$ swift post minerals
$ swift list
animals
minerals
vegetables
```

To get a listing of objects within a container, you can again use the list command, this time passing the container as a parameter:

```
$ swift list animals
lions.txt
tigers.txt
```

To upload objects to the cluster, you use the upload command, passing both the container and the object file name as parameters:

```
$ swift upload animals bears.txt
```

You can specify multiple files to upload in one command by passing additional parameters. If you specify a directory (folder) to upload instead of a file, all the files and directories within that directory will be uploaded, too.

Similarly, to download objects, use the download command, passing the container and object names as parameters:

```
$ swift download animals lions.txt
```

Finally, to remove an object from a container, use the delete command:

```
$ swift delete animals bears.txt
```

To remove a container and all the objects within it, pass only the container name:

```
$ swift delete animals
$ swift list
minerals
vegetables
```

As you can see, the delete command does not prompt for confirmation, and there is no way to restore objects once they have been deleted.

If you forget the commands available to you, running swift with no parameters will print a useful help message.

Command-line Tool for HPC: Swift Commander

Swift Commander was developed by Fred Hutchinson Cancer Research Center to be optimized for small-file workloads to archive and restore data sets in HPC environments. Swift Commander was written by the author of the postmark file system benchmark who is experienced building tools to handle small files.

Swift Commander is actively maintained and available at: *https:// github.com/FredHutch/swift-commander/*

Swift Commander, a simple shell wrapper for the swift client, curl, and some other tools makes working with swift very easy:

```
$ swc upload /my/posix/folder /my/swift/folder
$ swc compare /my/posix/folder /my/swift/folder
$ swc download /my/swift/folder /my/scratch/fs
```

Sub commands such as swc ls, swc cd, swc rm, swc more give you a feel that is similar to a Unix file system.

Swift Commander for HPC Archive

Lots of small files are problematic regardless of the storage system used. A common strategy is to create an archive of the entire directory structure via tar. However, in genomics research that single tar file can grow quite large.

The solution with Swift Commander is to create a tarball for each level:

```
/folder1.tar.gz
/folder1/folder2.tar.gz
/folder1/folder2/folder3.tar.gz
```

Restoring folder2 and below we just need folder2.tar.gz + folder3.tar.gz

Swift Commander also contains an archiving module:

```
$ archive:  swc arch /my/posix/folder /my/swift/
folder
$ restore:    swc unarch /my/swift/folder /my/
scratch/fs
```

With Swift Commander, the archiving module uses multiple processes. It has a measured performance of up to 400 MB/s from one Linux box. Each process uses pigz multithreaded gzip compression (Example: compressing 1GB DNA string down to 272MB: 111 sec using gzip, 5 seconds using pigz.) Restore can use standard gzip.

Desktop Tools

There are several tools which enable desktop users to connect to a SwiftStack cluster. Below are a few examples.

ExpanDrive

ExpanDrive provides a simple to install and use client for SwiftStack. It's a commercial product available for download at http://www.expandrive.com/expandrive

ExpanDrive supports Windows and Mac clients. Following installation, add a new drive and choose "OpenStack Swift Storage" as the drive type:

Adding a new drive Figure 7-2

Next, enter the AUTH address that can be found in the "Monitor" section of the SwiftStack controller under the "Cluster Health" tab under "Auth URL".

Enter the user credentials and choose a drive letter (Windows only) to map the account contents to.

Click "Save Changes" and "Connect."

The drive will be mapped within Windows Explorer or mounted in Finder.

Mapped drive in Windows Explorer (Windows) Figure 7-3

Mounted drive in Finder (OSX) Figure 7-4

Note: The ExpanDrive client will run in the system tray, even if a user closes the window.

Note: ExpanDrive has a known issue with self-signed certificates. A known workaround is available from ExpanDrive.

ExpanDrive can provide a branded solution for your organization
Figure 7-5

Cyberduck

Cyberduck is an open source tool for general purpose browse access to FTP, SFTP, WebDAV, and cloud storage. It is available for Apple Mac & Microsoft Windows platforms.

To be able to access a Swiftstack storage cluster Cyberduck needs to be configured in a particular manner. This describes how to install and use Cyberduck to access a Swiftstack storage cluster.

Cyberduck is available for download: *https://cyberduck.io/*
SwiftStack configuration profile: *https://trac.cyberduck.io/wiki/help/en/ howto/swiftstack*

Figure 7-6

To configure:

1. Download the HTTPS Cyberduck profile (or HTTP for test/ dev environments) located at https://trac.cyberduck.io/wiki/ help/en/howto/swiftstack
2. Double-click the file to launch Cyberduck and create a new bookmark for SwiftStack
3. Enter the SwiftStack cluster API IP address (from the "Con figure" tab in SwiftStack's controller interface) and your account name
4. Close the bookmark edit window to save your settings
5. Double-click the bookmark to open a connection and then enter your password

Cyberduck configuration on OSX Figure 7-7

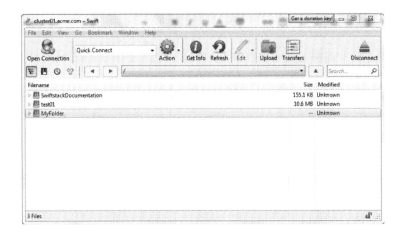

Cyberduck browser in Windows Figure 7-8

SwiftStack Filesystem Gateway

SwiftStack's Filesystem Gateway provides open and scalable file-based access to Swift. Adding a SwiftStack Gateway to a SwiftStack Cluster is fairly simple process. The server has the SwiftStack software installed with the same steps as installing a SwiftStack Node. However during the node ingestion on the SwiftStack Controller, the role of "SwiftStack Gateway" is chosen rather than "Swift node." Once designated as a Gateway, configuration options will be available.

A minimum hardware profile for a basic gateway would include two disks (one for caching) and two network interfaces.

Installation

Installation starts out the same as a SwiftStack Node, a process we expect anyone installing a Gateway will already be familiar with.

```
curl https://<controller hostname>/install | bash
```

After following the claim node process, select SwiftStack Gateway and click the "Ingest Now" button.

Ingesting a dedicated SwiftStack Filesystem Gateway Node Figure 7-9

There are several options that will need to be configured before you enable and then deploy the Gateway's configuration.

These options are found on the following pages:

- Auth tab
- Cache tab
- Settings tab - networking
- Shares tab

Configure Swift Account

Select the Swift Account section and provide the information for the Swift account that has been created as the service account for the Gateway.

This account allows the Gateway to access the Cluster and will be the primary auth for the containers where the NFS and CIFS/SMB files will be stored in Swift.

CIFS Settings

Click on the CIFS tab. On this page you will set the Gateway settings for all CIFS shares.

If "AD support" is needed, check the box. More configuration options will appear. Optionally, LDAP Settings can also be configured.

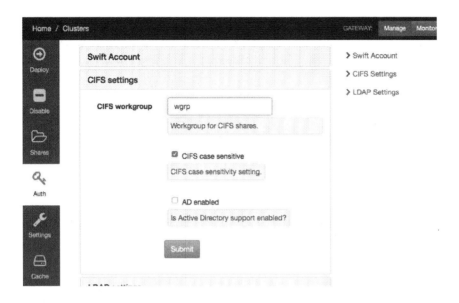

Configuring CIFS settings with the SwiftStack Controller Figure 7-10

Configuring Cache

On the Cache tab, you will need to format and assign one disk to be the Gateway's cache.

The cache provides a temporary staging area for the files delivered locally by the filesystem protocols (NFS and SMB/CIFS) as they are transferred to and from the Swift cluster. The cache effectively provides a network buffering area to handle the difference in the network speeds between client-to-gateway and gateway-to-cluster, caching frequently accessed files and providing filesystem semantics.

Two steps are needed to add a cache disk to the gateway for caching: formatting a disk and designating it as the cache.

Formatting

Locate the block device you wish to use for the filesystem cache. In its Cache Operation field, select "Format and mount" from the dropdown menu. Click the "Change" button.

Enabling Cache

Once the disk is formatted and mounted it will have the status of

Ready. The disk is now ready to be added as the gateway's cache. Again use the Cache Operation field, this time select "Use for Cache" from the dropdown menu. Click the "Change" button.

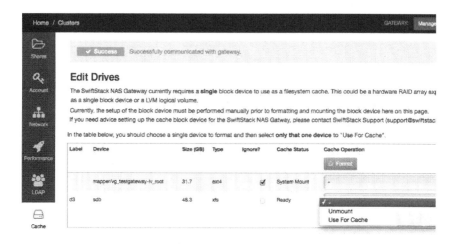

Configuring a cache with for a Filesystem Gateway Figure 7-11

Configuring Shares

On the Shares tab, you will map desired filesystem mount points to containers. Each share that you create will provide one mount point for one container — if you have three containers that need to have NFS access, you will be creating three shares. As your deployment matures it is likely that you will have numerous shares listed.

Currently the SwiftStack Filesystem Gateway supports the NFS (v3) and SMB (v2.1) protocols. We will show setting up an NFS share for one container and then setting up a SMB/CIFS share for another container.

Creating an NFS Share for a container

Click the "+ Create New Share" button. On the page that opens type in a name for the share, select the NFS protocol and type in the name of the container.

Creating an NFS Share Figure 7-12

Once completed, click on the "Add Gateway Share" button and the new share will now appear on the page.

Figure 7-13

Creating a CIFS Share for a container

Creating a CIFS share is a similar process. Again we will click the "+Create New Share" button. On the page that opens provide the following:

- Type the name of the share in the Name field: share name
- From the Protocol dropdown select: cifs
- From the Access mode dropdown select: rw
- Type in the name of the container in the "Swift container" field: container name
- Locate and check the Enabled box.

Enable Tab

At this point your Gateway is configured; it is time to enable and deploy it. On the Enable tab, click on the "Enable Gateway" button.

Enabling a Gateway Figure 7-14

Accessing your Gateway

Once you have a Gateway set up with at least one share, you will need to mount a share in order to use your Gateway.

Mounting CIFS Shares in Linux

To mount a CIFS share on a Linux server, run the following command:

```
mount -t cifs //$IP/$SHARENAME $DIR -o
user=$USER,password=$PASSWORD,uid=$UID,gid=$GID
```

Where:

- $IP is the IP or hostname of your Gateway
- $SHARENAME is the name of the share configured when

setting up your Gateway
- $SHARENAME is the name of the share you created earlier, not the name of the container that share will access.
- $DIR is the directory on the local system to mount the remote share on
- $USER and $PASSWORD are credentials for a user with per mission to authenticate against your Gateway

To find $UID and $GID, you can run the following commands. (Note: When the "CIFS id mapping" field is set to "rid", the commands will return nothing (No such user).)

```
id -g `whoami`
id -u `whoami`
```

Mounting Guest CIFS Shares in Linux

To mount a Guest CIFS share on a Linux server, run the following command:

```
mount   -t   cifs   //$IP/$SHARENAME   $DIR   -o
guest,uid=$UID,gid=$GID
```

Mounting CIFS Shares in OS X

To mount a CIFS share on an OS X server, run the following command:

```
mount -t smbfs
//$DOMAIN;$USER:$PASSWORD@$IP/$SHARENAME $DIR
or
mount   -t   smbfs   //$USER:$PASSWORD@$IP/$SHARENAME
$DIR
```

Where $DOMAIN is an optional Active Directory domain to use.

Mounting Guest CIFS Shares in OS X

To mount a Guest CIFS share on an OS X server, run the following command:

```
mount -t smbfs //guest:@$IP/$SHARENAME $DIR
```

Mounting NFS Shares in Linux or OS X

To mount a NFS share on a Linux or OS X server, use the following command:

```
mount -t nfs -o nfsvers=3 $IP:/share/$SHARE_NAME
$DIR
```

Where:
- $IP is the IP or hostname of your Gateway
- $SHARE_NAME is the name of the NFS share you are mounting
- $DIR is the directory on the local system where you want the remote share mounted.

Galaxy: Scientific Workflow Management

Galaxy is a web-based scientific workflow management software. It's targeted at research scientists that do not necessarily have computer programming experience so they can build and run multi-step computational analyses.

Galaxy can also be used as a data integration platform with SwiftStack. Data can be accessed via Swift API and Galaxy supports many file formats.

More information on downloading Galaxy: *http://galaxyproject.org/*
More information on using Galaxy: *https://usegalaxy.org/*

Galaxy in Use

Galaxy at Fred Hutchinson Cancer Research Center uses SwiftStack as primary storage in production today. Integrated with Slurm HPC scheduler (*http://slurm.schedmd.com/*), Galaxy automatically assigns default PI account (principal investigator) for each user.

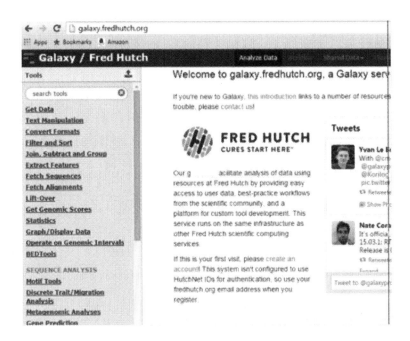

Galaxy at Fred Hutchinson Cancer Research Center Figure 7-15

Configuration Guide

Galaxy natively supports the OpenStack Swift API. Below is how to configure Galaxy to use the Swift API.

Clone source

```
$ git clone https://github.com/galaxyproject/
galaxy/
Cloning into 'galaxy'...
remote: Counting objects: 163694, done.
remote: Total 163694 (delta 0), reused 0 (delta 0),
pack-reused 163694
Receiving objects: 100% (163694/163694), 50.47 MiB
| 4.69 MiB/s, done.
Resolving deltas: 100% (130882/130882), done.

$ git checkout -b master origin/master
Branch master set up to track remote branch master
from origin.
Switched to a new branch 'master'
```

Configuration

Create config/galaxy.ini and config/object_store_conf.xml

```
$ cp config/galaxy.ini.sample  config/galaxy.ini
$ cp config/object_store_conf.xml.sample config/
object_store_conf.xml
```

Modify config/galaxy.ini. Modify the port number and host address that you want, and also don't forget to add object_store_config_file file for swift.

```
# The port on which to listen.
port = 8080

# The address on which to listen.  By default, only
listen to localhost (Galaxy
# will not be accessible over the network).  Use
'0.0.0.0' to listen on all
# available network interfaces.
host = 0.0.0.0

...
# -- Data Storage (Object Store)
#
# Configuration file for the object store
# If this is set and exists, it overrides any other
objectstore settings.
object_store_config_file = config/object_store_conf.
xml

# Object store backend module (valid options are:
disk, s3, swift, irods,
# distributed, hierarchical)

...
```

Modify config/object_store_conf.xml Please add this section for swift and fill all parameters.

```
<!-- Sample Swift Object Store -->
        <object_store type="swift" id="primary"
order="2">
                <auth access_key="...." secret_
key="....." />
                <bucket name="unique_bucket_name"
use_reduced_redundancy="False"          max_chunk_
size="250"/>
        <connection host="" port="" is_secure=""
conn_path="" multipart="True"/>
        <cache path="database/files/" size="1000"
/>
        </object_store>
```

Here is a sample config file for support swift.
Primary 0: Swift
Primary 1: distributed
Secondary 2: disk

```
<?xml version="1.0"?>
<object_store type="hierarchical">
    <backends>
     <object_store type="distributed" id="primary"
order="1">
            <backends>
                <backend id="files1" type="disk"
weight="1">
                <files_dir path="database/files1"/>
                    <extra_dir type="temp"
path="database/tmp1"/>
                    <extra_dir type="job_work"
path="database/job_working_directory1"/>
                </backend>
                <backend id="files2" type="disk"
weight="1">
                <files_dir path="database/files2"/>
                    <extra_dir type="temp"
```

```
                   path="database/tmp2"/>
                          <extra_dir type="job_work"
     path="database/job_working_directory2"/>
                   </backend>
              </backends>
         </object_store>
          <object_store type="disk" id="secondary"
     order="2">
              <files_dir path="database/files3"/>
              <extra_dir type="temp" path="database/
     tmp3"/>
          <extra_dir type="job_work" path="database/
     job_working_directory3"/>
          </object_store>

          <!-- Sample Swift Object Store -->
          <object_store type="swift" id="primary"
     order="0">
                   <auth access_key="demo" secret_
     key="6f31c3bb248f537c8f27742a465f78db" />
                   <bucket name="swift_backend" use_
     reduced_redundancy="False" max_chunk_size="250"/>
                   <connection host="192.168.200.23"
     port="80"     is_secure="False"     conn_path=""
     multipart="True"/>
              <cache path="database/files/" size="1000"
     />
          </object_store>

     </backends>
     </object_store>
```

Run Galaxy Server

Now, we can execute run.sh to bring galaxy server up and check if it works with swift.

```
$ sh run.sh
Initializing  config/migrated_tools_conf.xml  from
```

```
migrated_tools_conf.xml.sample
Initializing config/shed_tool_conf.xml from shed_
tool_conf.xml.sample
Initializing config/shed_tool_data_table_conf.xml
from shed_tool_data_table_conf.xml.sample
Initializing config/shed_data_manager_conf.xml from
shed_data_manager_conf.xml.sample

...

galaxy.objectstore.s3 DEBUG 2015-03-23 10:26:43,516
Configuring Swift Connection
galaxy.objectstore.s3 DEBUG 2015-03-23 10:26:43,531
Using cloud object store with bucket 'swift_
backend'
galaxy.objectstore.s3 INFO 2015-03-23 10:26:43,532
Cache cleaner manager started
galaxy.objectstore DEBUG 2015-03-23 10:26:43,545
Loading backends for distributed object store from
primary
galaxy.objectstore DEBUG 2015-03-23 10:26:43,546
Loaded disk backend 'files1' with weight 1 and file_
path: database/files1
galaxy.objectstore DEBUG 2015-03-23 10:26:43,546
Extra directories:
galaxy.objectstore DEBUG 2015-03-23 10:26:43,546
job_work: database/job_working_directory1
galaxy.objectstore DEBUG 2015-03-23 10:26:43,546
temp: database/tmp1
galaxy.objectstore DEBUG 2015-03-23 10:26:43,546
Loaded disk backend 'files2' with weight 1 and file_
path: database/files2
galaxy.objectstore DEBUG 2015-03-23 10:26:43,547
Extra directories:
galaxy.objectstore DEBUG 2015-03-23 10:26:43,547
job_work: database/job_working_directory2
galaxy.objectstore DEBUG 2015-03-23 10:26:43,547
temp: database/tmp2
```

...

```
galaxy.queue_worker INFO 2015-03-23 10:26:48,434
Initalizing     Galaxy     Queue     Worker     on
sqlalchemy+sqlite:///./database/control.
sqlite?isolation_level=IMMEDIATE
Starting server in PID 2857.
serving on 0.0.0.0:8080 view at http://127.0.0.1:8080
```

When you saw those lines in log as follows, that means that galaxy is connected to the swift cluster and already created a container called swift_backend.

```
galaxy.objectstore.s3 DEBUG 2015-03-23 10:26:43,516
Configuring Swift Connection
galaxy.objectstore.s3 DEBUG 2015-03-23 10:26:43,531
Using  cloud  object  store  with  bucket  'swift_
backend'
galaxy.objectstore DEBUG 2015-03-23 10:26:43,545
Loading backends for distributed object store from
primary
```

Let's check the status of swift_backend via python swiftclient.

```
$ swift -v stat swift_backend
                URL: http://192.168.200.23/v1/AUTH_
demo/swift_backend
   Auth Token: AUTH_tkdee051284fff41e89b9269d0b49b8597
        Account: AUTH_demo
      Container: swift_backend
        Objects: 0
          Bytes: 0
       Read ACL:
      Write ACL:
        Sync To:
       Sync Key:
  Accept-Ranges: bytes
X-Storage-Policy: Standard-Replica
     Connection: keep-alive
    X-Timestamp: 1427104426.10102
```

```
X-Trans-Id: txef9294899d17454293f1f-00550fe6a7
Content-Type: text/plain; charset=utf-8
```

Upload file to Galaxy

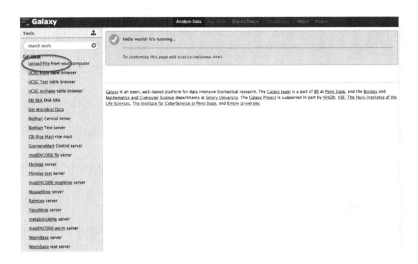

Uploading a file to Galaxy Figure 7-16

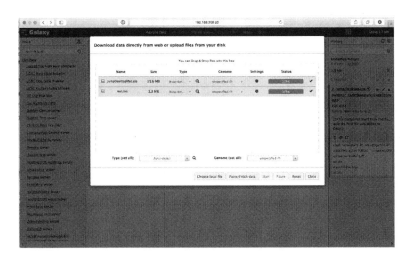

Downloading a file with Galaxy Figure 7-17

Let's verify the files in the swift cluster.

```
$ swift -v stat swift_backend
            URL: http://192.168.200.23/v1/AUTH_
```

```
demo/swift_backend
  Auth Token: AUTH_tkdee051284fff41e89b9269d0b49b8597
        Account: AUTH_demo
      Container: swift_backend
        Objects: 2
          Bytes: 1327762
       Read ACL:
      Write ACL:
        Sync To:
       Sync Key:
  Accept-Ranges: bytes
X-Storage-Policy: Standard-Replica
     Connection: keep-alive
    X-Timestamp: 1427104426.10102
     X-Trans-Id: txed03062ddbcd42f984216-00550fecfd
   Content-Type: text/plain; charset=utf-8


$ swift -v list swift_backend
000/dataset_2.dat
000/dataset_3.dat


$ swift -v stat swift_backend 000/dataset_2.dat
            URL: http://192.168.200.23/v1/AUTH_demo/
swift_backend/000/dataset_2.dat
  Auth Token: AUTH_tkdee051284fff41e89b9269d0b49b8597
        Account: AUTH_demo
      Container: swift_backend
         Object: 000/dataset_2.dat
   Content Type: application/x-ns-proxy-autoconfig
 Content Length: 24683
  Last Modified: Mon, 23 Mar 2015 10:28:15 GMT
           ETag: ba580616354c6407a5985c11242f4530
  Accept-Ranges: bytes
     Connection: keep-alive
    X-Timestamp: 1427106494.78104
     X-Trans-Id: tx53fdb57d4c924c6b9fe7e-00550ff058


$ swift -v stat swift_backend 000/dataset_3.dat
```

```
          URL: http://192.168.200.23/v1/AUTH_demo/
   swift_backend/000/dataset_3.dat
   Auth Token: AUTH_tkdee051284fff41e89b9269d0b49b8597
      Account: AUTH_demo
    Container: swift_backend
       Object: 000/dataset_3.dat
 Content Type: application/x-ns-proxy-autoconfig
Content Length: 1303079
Last Modified: Mon, 23 Mar 2015 10:31:11 GMT
         ETag: 12e9bd6acc76e3fd408bfa82a8b5003a
Accept-Ranges: bytes
   Connection: keep-alive
  X-Timestamp: 1427106670.54420
   X-Trans-Id: tx2477792500fb4743899e3-00550ff05d
```

CommVault Simpana: Backup

CommVault Simpana users can migrate their tape and traditional storage targets to SwiftStack. CommVault Simpana provides archiving, backup, snapshot management, and reporting. Using SwiftStack as a storage target enables IT organizations to reclaim space on primary storage. With SwiftStack CommVault users can geographically distribute backup data to store backups across multiple datacenters, which provides more options when recovering from a disaster.

Best Practice Recommendations

Multiple Storage Libraries

To ensure that performance is not impacted as additional clients are added, it is recommended that multiple Storage Libraries backed by SwiftStack are created in a CommVault Simpana Storage Policy. Each Storage Library should be mapped to a dedicated container in the SwiftStack Object Storage System and the Storage Policy should be configured to use multiple data paths in a round-robin fashion allowing the backup load to be spread across the storage system.

Data Pruning

CommVault Simpana uses a "chunk-based" storage scheme for storing data and may combine data from numerous clients into objects stored in SwiftStack. Some features in Simpana, such as Data Aging, use a "pruning" method to remove bytes of data from the chunks as needed based on configured policies. However, since the SwiftStack Object Storage System supports operations on entire objects, Simpana will "flag" the byte range within the chunks for pruning and an object will not be removed until all of the chunks that comprise the object have been flagged for removal.

Since data is stored as whole objects in the SwiftStack Object Storage System, storage utilization with the current supported version(s) of Simpana is not as granular as block-based storage technologies. To optimize the utilization, we recommend combining backups and archives for applications/clients requiring the same retention policies to dedicated Simpana Storage Policies. This will make it more likely that all bytes in a given object will eventually be a candidate for pruning and will be deleted to free up capacity.

SwiftStack Storage Policies

A storage policy in CommVault Simpana is primarily used to map data from clients to a storage backend for backup and recovery operations. However, SwiftStack also includes a storage policy feature that is used to organize data based on location, storage media, and data protection scheme across the storage system.

Storage policies in SwiftStack can be used to distribute data off-site for disaster recovery capabilities. To take advantage of this feature, you must ensure that the containers in a Simpana Storage Library are associated with a SwiftStack Storage Policy that will store data in different regions or locations. For this configuration, it is recommended that the "Write Affinity" feature is turned on in SwiftStack to enable Simpana to write data locally - to meet your backup windows, for example - and the data will eventually be distributed throughout the storage system. However, if data cannot reside in certain locations due to regulations or policies, you can apply a SwiftStack Storage Policy to the appropriate SwiftStack containers to ensure that the data will reside in a specific location.

Configuration Guide

For a full configuration guide see: *https://swiftstack.com/partners/*

Adding a cloud storage library in CommVault Simpana Figure 7-18

Conclusion

In this chapter we have introduced some applications for accessing SwiftStack clusters that are of particular use to life sciences. If you choose to use one of these applications and are uncertain about any aspect, we encourage you to seek out additional instruction and documentation. The next and final chapter considers hardware requirements and best practices for deploying OpenStack Swift with SwiftStack.

## Chapter Eight

Hardware Deployment with SwiftStack

In this chapter, we take a brief look at the hardware requirements of deploying OpenStack Swift with SwiftStack to handle the workloads required of genomics. While we will provide some guidelines below, SwiftStack works with systems vendors to ensure that the hardware matches the needs of the specific deployment.

As we learned in the previous chapters, Swift is designed to store and retrieve files across a cluster of industry-standard servers and drives, using replication to ensure data reliability and fault tolerance. While this model enables you to take advantage of lower-cost hardware, it requires upfront planning, validation, and testing to ensure that suitable hardware is selected.

Selecting Hardware

SwiftStack works with several vendors who provide hardware solutioı for OpenStack Swift. This ranges from qualified chassis from majɾ OEM partners to pre-integrated racks from recommended VARs.

When selecting hardware for your Swift cluster, it is important tı determine which configuration provides the best balance of IC performance, capacity, and cost for your workload. For instance, ɛ cluster that is primarily interfacing with sequencers and an HPC clusteı will have a different profile than one that is used primarily for archiving.

Since SwiftStack can be run on a wide range of hardware configurations, we have built benchmarking tools such as SwiftStack-bench (*https://github.com/swiftstack/ssbench*). These tools can ensure that the entire system (hardware and software) will fulfill the workload.

For more information about our hardware partners and specific recommendations please contact us by visiting: *https://swiftstack.com/contact-us/*

Architecture Overview

In most clusters, there are at least two hardware types: proxy nodes and storage nodes. The SwiftStack package-based installer contains both proxy server components and storage server components, which can

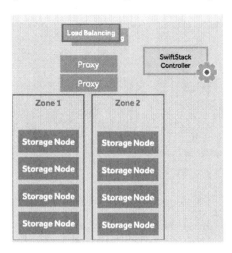

Components of a SwiftStack deployment Figure 8-1

either be run on the same physical node for smaller clusters or be split out in separate tiers for larger deployments. For larger-scale and high-performance clusters, the account and container metadata tier can also be split out into a separate hardware layer, leveraging high-performance media, such as SSDs.

Networking

When planning a Swift deployment, attention also needs to be paid to how the networking is set up and configured. While all networking in a Swift cluster is done via Layer-3, a Swift cluster will have several different network segments.

First is a front-facing network for API access. If an external load balancer is used you'll need to consider how you will accomodate this. Second, a storage network serving the proxy nodes' communication to the storage nodes and communication between the storage nodes. A route to a SwiftStack Controller. For an on-premise SwiftStack Controller, this would be an internal route. For the SwiftStack Controller Service, this would be a route to platform.swiftstack.com. A management network for IPMI, iLO, etc. used for hardware management.

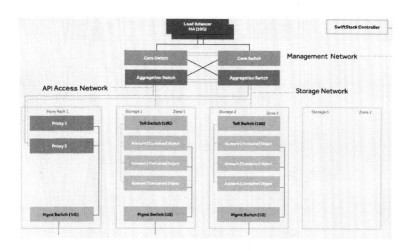

Example Networks for SwiftStack Figure 8-2

The Proxy Tier

Proxy nodes handle all incoming API requests. Once a proxy server receives a request, it will determine which storage node to connect to based on the URL of the object. When a client uploads data to SwiftStack, the proxy tier will write data simultaneously to multiple storage nodes.

Proxy services also coordinate responses, handle failures, and do the computation required for erasure coding. As the proxy tier uses a shared-nothing architecture, it can be scaled as needed based on projected workloads. If separated into its own tier, a minimum of two nodes should be deployed in the proxy tier for redundancy. Should one proxy node fail, the other(s) will take over.

Having the proxy services in their own tier enables read/write access to be scaled out independently of storage capacity. For example, if the cluster has high demand for data access, many proxy nodes can be provisioned. However, if the cluster is being used primarily for archival purposes, fewer proxy nodes are needed.

Proxy Node Caching

While the proxy node does not cache objects, it does use its cache to store other data to improve performance. For example, the proxy nodes:

- Cache information about an account including the list of its containers
- Cache container data – list of its objects and access-control list information
- Store cname lookups so that an account url can be mapped to a hostname
- Store static web data (index, css, for example)
- Store authentication tokens
- Keep track of client requests when rate limiting is enabled

Load Balancing

SwiftStack is configured with a built-in load balancer which is enabled when "Use SwiftStack Load Balancer" is checked on the cluster configuration page. Each node that is serving the proxy will share a Virtual IP and must be on the same layer-2 network as the other proxy nodes. Each proxy node is listening for who is taking load-balancing responsibilities and if one of the proxy nodes goes down, another will take responsibility.

Alternatively, an external load balancer may be configured.

Either way, a SwiftStack cluster will coordinate with the load balancer when performing rolling upgrades, disabling nodes for maintenance to ensure requests are appropriately routed during system maintenance.

Proxy Hardware

The proxy nodes use a moderate amount of RAM and are network IO intensive. Typically, proxy servers are 1U systems. For small Swift clusters, the storage services and proxy services can run on the same physical nodes.

As these systems field each incoming API request, it is wise to provision them with two high-throughput (10GbE) interfaces. One interface is used for 'front-end,' incoming requests and the other for 'back-end' access to the storage nodes to put and fetch data.

For proxy nodes, we recommend running at 24 GB of RAM for system processes.

The Storage Tier

The storage tier in a Swift cluster is, naturally, where all the data resides. This tier runs all the storage services for the cluster. This includes:

- Services to store and serve accounts, containers, and objects
- Replication services for accounts, containers, and objects
- Auditing processes for accounts, containers, and objects
- Auditors to keep containers and accounts up-to-date
- Reconstructors to audit erasure coded objects

Storage Hardware

Object storage nodes are typically configured as high-density nodes ranging from 12-drive 1U systems, to 84-drives in 5U. These nodes use a reasonable amount of memory and CPU. The storage nodes run services not only to field incoming requests from the proxy nodes, but also run services for replication, auditing, and other processes to ensure durability. Storage nodes can be provisioned with single gigabit or 10GbE network interface depending on expected workload and desired performance.

Do not use RAID

Swift replicates data across disks, nodes, zones, and regions, so there is no need for the data redundancy provided by a RAID controller. Parity based RAID, such as RAID5, RAID6, and RAID10, harms the performance of a cluster and does not provided any additional protection because Swift is already providing data redundancy.

Example Configuration

The following description of a SwiftStack genomics deployment shows how the previous hardware guidelines might play out in practice. This particular deployment stores FASTQ, BAM, and VCF data generated by Illumina HiSeq X Ten sequencers and the related software applications which process, align, and analyze that data. In this configuration, approximately one petabyte of usable capacity is on-site near the genomic sequencers and is accessed both by applications using the native Swift API and via NFS and CIFS using the SwiftStack Filesystem Gateway. An additional 200 terabytes of usable capacity is also available in two remote locations (i.e. regions) for distribution of BAM and VCF files to scientists who perform additional analysis in outside facilities. All three sites participate in the same multi-region Swift cluster, and storage policies allow control over what data is distributed to which remote locations.

Primary Site

The primary site contains the following hardware with the specifications indicated:

- On-Premise Controller (x2)
  - 1u server
  - 32GB DRAM
  - 2x 4-core CPUs
  - 2x 200GB HDDs (RAID-1 for operating system)
  - 4x 200GB SSDs (RAID-10 for telemetry data)

- Filesystem Gateway (x3)
  - 2u server
  - 64GB DRAM
  - 2x 4-core CPUs
  - 2x 200GB HDDs (RAID-1 for operating system)
  - Embedded PCIe RAID card
  - 8x 1TB HDDs (RAID-6, resulting in approximately 6TB usable)
  - 2x 10GbE dual-port NIC

- PAC — Proxy/Account/Container Node (x3)
  - 1u server
  - 64GB DRAM
  - 2x 8-core CPUs
  - 2x 200GB HDDs (RAID-1 for operating system)
  - 2x 200GB SSD (for Account/Container data)
  - 2x 10GbE dual-port NIC

- O — Object Storage Node (x14)
  - 4u server
  - 128GB DRAM
  - 2x Intel E5-2650 CPUs
  - 2x 200GB HDDs (RAID-1 for operating system)
  - 1x 10GbE dual-port NIC
  - 4x 1GbE on-board NIC ports
  - 1x SAS HBA
  - 36x 6TB HDDs

Remote Sites

The two remote sites contain identical hardware as described here:

- PAC — Proxy/Account/Container Node (x3)
  - 1u server

- ○ 64GB DRAM
- ○ 2x 8-core CPUs
- ○ 2x 200GB HDDs (RAID-1 for operating system)
- ○ 2x 200GB SSD (for Account/Container data)
- ○ 2x 10GbE dual-port NIC

- **O — Object Storage Node (x3)**
  - ○ 4u server
  - ○ 128GB DRAM
  - ○ 2x Intel E5-2650 CPUs
  - ○ 2x 200GB HDDs (RAID-1 for operating system)
  - ○ 1x 10GbE dual-port NIC
  - ○ 4x 1GbE on-board NIC ports
  - ○ 1x SAS HBA
  - ○ 36x 6TB HDDs

Conclusion

In this chapter you've learned about some general hardware guidelines for nodes and some of the devices needed for the different network segments of a Swift cluster. As always, there's no one-size-fits-all solution, so be sure to carefully consider your use case and the optimal components for your needs. Still, as long as you don't make major, fundamental mistakes in your networking setup, the beauty of Swift is that it will allow for networking changes. Even if you configure your networking one way, you can relatively easily adjust it later to meet expansion or segmentation needs. If you plan network changes carefully, you can make the changes without any cluster downtime.

Afterword

We're moving into a future of increased genomics and bioinformatics activity. In not too many years sequencing of patient genomes may well be commonplace.

At SwiftStack we think a lot about how to store unstructured data. We're confident that the future of genomics data storage will be increasingly open source and standards-based. We very much look forward to being part of that future, helping organizations store and use the data that will drive clinical and research innovation.

As you put this book to use and work with Swift and SwiftStack, we invite your comments, feedback, and suggestions. Please let us know what we need to correct or add; share your insights; and help us create a resource that will serve you better. You can do so by visiting *http://swiftstack.com/books/Object-Storage-for-Genomics*.

Thanks!